YOUNG THACK

Books by Jean Gould

MISS EMILY

JANE

YOUNG THACK

YOUNG THACK

(*William Makepeace Thackeray*)

By Jean Gould

Illustrated with
Thackeray's original sketches

HOUGHTON MIFFLIN COMPANY · BOSTON
The Riverside Press Cambridge
1949

The Riverside Press

CAMBRIDGE · MASSACHUSETTS

PRINTED IN THE U.S.A.

Contents

List of Illustrations

The illustrations facing pages 70, 71, 182, and 198 are from original sketches by Thackeray in the Henry W. and Albert A. Berg Collection of the New York Public Library. The illustration facing page 199 is included by permission of the Huntington Library, San Marino, California.

YOUNG THACK

I

Away to England

WHEN HE LOOKED BACK, he could see his mother standing at the top of the landing-place, waving her white
lace handkerchief. He could see her lips moving to form
the words, "Good-bye, Billy!" but he could no longer hear
her. By now they were too far down the river stair or *ghaut,*
which led from the high bank of the city to the docks below.
They were almost at the bottom, where the boat was waiting
to take him and his cousin away to England — far away from
Calcutta, where he had been born on July 18, 1811, and had
lived all six years of his life.

"Have care, Sahib." The native attendant took his elbow
as he turned on the last step of the ghaut to cast a final upward glance, thereby blocking the path of other passengers
who were descending. His mother's white parasol was like a
halo around her dark curls.

He waved briefly, and, for fear of tears, ran quickly after
his cousin, already on the dock. Two small leather trunks,
marked "William M. Thackeray, Fareham, Hampshire," and
"Richmond Shakespear, London," stood among the luggage
to be placed on board. There was the usual bustle of em-
barkation: officials asking for passports; travellers anxious
over tickets, baggage, boxes, and small babies; crewmen singing out orders, pulling ropes, hauling loads down into the
hold. And all about, a crowd of dusky natives milled over
the wharf in hopes of a few pennies to be gained selling
souvenirs, begging, or snatching at a dropped coin.

"Hurry up, Bill," Richmond was impatient to climb the

gangplank. "Good-bye, Ma!" he called once again to the figure beside Mrs. Thackeray on the shore.

"Good-bye, Mamma," faltered William, half to himself because he mustn't let Richmond know the way he was feeling. On a sudden impulse he took after his cousin. "Race you to the top, Rich!" He struck out toward the high end of the gangplank ahead of Richmond, who accepted the challenge willingly once he had recovered from surprise.

The two scampered up the bridge in advance of the startled native who was taking care of them. They pushed and shoved each other, and squeezed past the line of grownups filing into the boat, both of them determined to reach the top first. A French poodle, held tightly in his mistress's arms, barked excitedly, and with an unexpected leap, jumped to the floor, where it created great confusion among the passengers, snapping at trouser legs and nipping the ladies' skirts.

The native, his nostrils dilating with astonishment, came on in pursuit of his charges. "Stay, Sahib, stay! You are not to run away. Hold. Stay!"

A man cursed, a woman screamed when the little dog tore her gown, while its owner shouted frantically, "Fifi, Fifi, come back, I say, come back!"

When the uproar was at its height, the attendant managed to reach his charges who were grinning like monkeys. He picked a boy up under each arm and stalked back to the end of the line with them. A sailor, meanwhile, restored the French poodle to its owner, and calm returned as the passengers boarded the boat.

Once on deck, the turbaned nurse, still holding William and Richmond securely under his arms, walked to the rail and bade them turn their eyes toward shore. "Say farewell to India, a last farewell to your mothers," he told them. "It is in Allah's hands whether you will see them again."

Sobered, the boys gazed at the towers and cupolas of Calcutta shining in the white, hot sunlight of India behind the row of people on the shore. "How *little* Mamma looks!" thought William. "Like the great doll Polly plays with." (Polly Graham was another cousin, three years younger than he, who lived in Calcutta with her parents.)

Some miles distant, at Alipur, was the home he had to leave, a big country lodge with a flat roof like a porch. At this moment brown-skinned Betty might be laying the towels out to dry up there, and he would be allowed to go along and play. Perched on his shoulder, Jocko, his pet monkey, would chatter and screech for joy at the sight of the ledge around which the creature loved to scramble, going precariously near the rim. Sometimes he would pretend to fall over the side, and hang by his tail until Billy rescued him. Then he would hug the boy's head and twist the brown curls with impish delight. It had cost Billy a good many tears to leave Jocko behind in Calcutta. If he could have taken his pet along, it would have been like taking part of India with him, but there was no place for a monkey at his great-grandmother's.

Occasionally when they were on the roof at home, his mother would come up, and they would lean on the ledge, idly viewing the gardens below, the terrace, and the sloping road that led to the narrow, winding streets of Alipur. When the fanlike shadows of the palm trees lengthened on the terrace walk, they would go down and join his father for tea — his tall, quiet, poetic-looking father, who would greet them with a grave smile and few words. As Collector of Calcutta, Mr. Thackeray was always surrounded with business documents — mysterious papers they were to William. The little boy and his mother would take their tea almost in silence, while Mr. Thackeray rustled his papers and sipped his steaming cup. Presently he would pat his son on the head, say a word or two to Mrs. Thackeray, and leave them. William and his mother would walk in the gardens until it was time for his ayah to come to put him to bed.

That was before his father died, nearly two years ago. He had come down with the deadly fever everyone in India feared, and the doctors could not save him.

Lately, Captain Carmichael-Smyth had been coming to tea. He was a big, splendidly turned-out man with a row of medals across his chest. He had an unlimited store of tales to tell, and he was always ready to entertain William with one of them. He would play catch, too, or ride you about on his shoulders. Teatime was lengthened now, and seven o'clock, when the ayah appeared and Mrs. Thackeray said, "Time for bed, Billy," seemed to come upon him in five minutes.

The twilight picture faded, and he realized that the shoreline was growing smaller and smaller as the ship moved down the Hooghly River toward the Ganges. He didn't want to leave India, the only home he knew; he didn't want to leave his mother to go to school in England. His mother was coming later, when "matters were settled," she explained, but he was of school age now, and all British children born in India were sent to England for their education. Nevertheless, he didn't want to go. He buried his head in the attendant's shoulder until the *Prince Regent* was well on her way. He didn't care to see the world he had known dwindle to nothing.

There was not much to do on board. Unfortunately, Cousin Richmond was taken with seasickness after the first day out, so Billy was forced to find his own amusements, and they were few. If the sea weren't too rough, he could walk around the deck, and chase the fat lady's French poodle, and watch her go toddling after it, screaming. Or he could sit on the sidelines during a game of shuffleboard and try to pick out which man would win. Or in the cabin at mealtimes, wait to see if the old general with the drooping white mustaches like a walrus's would get through the meal without dipping them in his tea. But on the whole the voyage was not as exciting as he had expected. He wished it were over.

One morning the *Prince Regent* put in at a small island in the South Atlantic for supplies. The coast was rocky, wild, and deserted. As he stood by his servant's side watching the sailors make fast the moorings, William wondered who would live on such an island.

"What is it called?" he wanted to know.

"St. Helena." The Indian took his hand, and led him toward the gangplank. "Come, we are going ashore. You shall see him."

"Who? Whom shall I see?" Billy hopped on one foot and peered over the side.

"A man — a strange, fierce, wicked man."

"Why is he wicked? What is his name?"

"I will tell you when we see him, my little one." The Indian would say no more, but, once they had descended the gangplank and crossed the small landing place, he struck out along the first road, taking such broad strides Billy could hardly keep up with him.

They walked what seemed an endless way, over rocks and hills, across barren fields and stretches of sand until at last they reached an iron fence, surrounding a garden. The man stopped by the fence, his eyes alert, his body still.

"Why are we waiting here?" Billy jerked his hand. "Let's go in."

"Sh." The servant frowned
disapprovingly. "We cannot
go in. But if we wait, he may
walk this way, and we can see
him."

"Who? Who?"

"Sh-h-h. Wait . . ."

A moment later a man came
out of a small summerhouse
toward them down the garden
path. He moved restlessly, his
hands clasped behind his back,
his head down, as if he had
been tramping and pondering
for hours, for days.

An Exile

"That is he," said the black man. "That is Bonaparte!
He eats three sheep every day, and all the little children he
can lay his hands on." He whispered the last words, rolling
his eyes upward.

William, not afraid, but curious, stared hard at the uniformed figure on the other side of the iron bars. What a
strange military hat the man wore, what a long scabbard and
sword. Why was he dressed for a parade here on this empty
island? Did he really eat little children?

There was no answer to these questions — the Indian
whisked William away after a few seconds. But the boy had
a feeling, as they went back on the lonely road to the ship,
that he would never forget the sight of that strange, pre-
occupied soldier, walking alone in the garden.

Four weeks later the ship, *Prince Regent,* arrived in England.

2

New Family Faces

SINCE RICHMOND had been ill through most of the voyage, the Indian attendant decided to go to the Ritchies' first, where William's cousin was to be left. Mrs. Ritchie had been Charlotte Thackeray before her marriage, a sister to William's father and Richmond's mother. Both boys spoke of her as "my Aunt Ritchie."

It was night when they reached London, and they were both too tired to do more than blink with wonder at the myriad lights gleaming from the amusement halls, inns, clubs, theatres, the blazing chandeliers glimpsed in the great town houses, the candles winking from nearly every window of the closely built homes of the huge, sprawling city. William wished he were not so sleepy so that he might take it all in. He rubbed his eyes in an effort to keep them open. "I'm going to ask my Aunt Ritchie to take us for a ride tomorrow so we can see what these buildings are. Look, Rich, do you s'pose that's Westminster Abbey?" But his cousin had dropped off to sleep, his head on the Indian's shoulder.

The Ritchies lived in Southampton Row in a big, comfortable apartment above Mr. Ritchie's place of business, which occupied the lower floor. Aunt Ritchie, who was waiting for the boys as they came up the stairs, seemed to match the apartment perfectly — she was a big, comfortable woman, with a big, sweet face and a slow smile.

She hugged both boys to her at once. "Welcome to England, my dear nephews!" She drew back to look them over. "You're Richmond," she decided correctly, "and," she turned

7

to Billy, "you must be William Makepeace Thackeray. What a lot of name for a little boy!" She laughed, a lazy, indolent, musical laugh, like the leisurely bubbling of a rich syrup.

"You have a great look of my papa," William said, "only he never laughed much. I like the way you laugh."

"I'm glad you do." The slow smile came again. "My poor brother Richmond, I don't think India ever agreed with him! You have the look of your papa, too," she took Billy's face in her hands. "I hope you will be like him."

"You mean, have a lot of papers around and be busy all the time?"

Aunt Ritchie laughed again. "Not exactly." She scanned Richmond's face now. "And you rather resemble your mother. I suppose all the Thackerays look more or less alike. And there are a great many of us, you will discover! Some of your uncles will be coming to see you. But you're both half dead for sleep. You must have something to eat and go to bed."

While they were drinking the warm milk and demolishing a plate of biscuits brought in by a red-cheeked maidservant, their uncle John Ritchie came up from below. He, too, welcomed them to the homeland of their parents, and if he wasn't as easy to know as Aunt Ritchie, he was no less kind. "You must consider this your London home," he told the boys. "We shall always be glad to see you."

It was a comfort to be received by such relatives. William had dreaded the day the boat landed, when he would be in a strange land, meeting all the members of his parents' family, but here at the Ritchies' he felt at home immediately. A sweet drowsiness overcame him almost as soon as he climbed into the high bed beside his cousin, and he went to sleep with no more than a fleeting picture of his mother crossing his mind.

He awoke the next morning full of eagerness to see the great city of London. "Rich!" He leaned over and shook his cousin. "Wake up. Maybe my Aunt Ritchie will take us for a drive today. I hope she and my uncle keep a carriage."

They did, as Mrs. Ritchie informed the boys when she appeared shortly with little William, a sturdy baby of eight months, in her arms. "I usually give the baby an airing on these fine afternoons," she said. "I think we will surely go today. Would you like to come along?" Her eyes twinkled; she knew the question was unnecessary.

To the boys who sat in the back of the carriage on small seats across from their aunt and uncle and the baby, London in the middle of June, 1817, was all wonder and enchantment. William kept turning his head from one side to the other for fear of missing something. He had seen various pictures of the city when he was in Calcutta. Before he went to sleep his ayah had often turned over the pages of the pictorial history of England one of his uncles had sent. But he had not expected there would be so many buildings, or that the town would be spread out over such an immense area, or that so many people crowded its streets.

They drove along Pall Mall and saw the dandies riding horseback in Rotten Row. "Why is it called that?" William had to know. It was a funny name for a fashionable promenade.

"Because it runs by the banks of the Serpentine Canal there, you see," his uncle pointed out the winding canal, "and they used to be infested with rats."

"Are the rats gone now?"

"Oh, mostly, I expect." His uncle smiled.

The answer was something of a disappointment to six-year-old William. The drive continued. They traversed the Thames, saw the Tower of London, Westminster Abbey;

and as they neared a lofty cathedral, its dome and spires rising into the blue, Billy felt the sudden thrill of recognition. He called out to everybody: "That is St. Paul's!"

Mr. and Mrs. Ritchie looked at each other in surprise.

"You're quite correct, dear," his aunt nodded approvingly. "How did you know?"

"I've seen pictures of it in a book the ayah used to show me."

"And you were able to spot it? Good going for a chap your age!" His uncle did not conceal his admiration for his new-found nephew, and William's chest swelled: he wagered he knew London better than anyone who'd never been there before.

"I'd have known the other places, too, if you hadn't told me," he bragged.

"O-ho, I think the boy's head is getting too large for him," remarked his uncle. "He'll be needing a man-size hat soon!"

The boys laughed, and William, in high glee, took his uncle's tall hat from the carriage arm on which it was resting, and plumped it on the back of his curly mop of hair.

Richmond roared, and the baby reached out his chubby hands to grab the hat himself. His mother and father were smiling indulgently at the fun when Mrs. Ritchie noticed a strange fact. "Look, John," she put her hand on her husband's arm. "Your hat quite fits my nephew!"

It was true — the topper sat as snugly on William as if it belonged to him. He had an exceptionally large head for a boy of six, made even larger by the mass of light brown curls, and his big moon face with the mild, grey-blue eyes set wide apart added to the effect of unusual size. In contrast, his body was thin and rather rangy.

Aunt Ritchie was alarmed once the over-size of William's head had been brought to her attention. "We must take him to see Sir Charles Clarke." She would hear no suggestion of delay, but gave orders to the coachman to drive to the noted physician's office.

The doctor examined William thoroughly, and asked him a good many questions. His age, his place of birth, and so on. When he learned that Billy had just arrived in England, he leaned forward in his chair. "Was it a good voyage? Tell me all about it."

"Well, sir, I thought it was a good voyage," William didn't know exactly what the doctor wanted to hear. "We made it in four months and eleven days, but Richmond — that's my cousin who came with me — got seasick, so we couldn't have much fun on board. The boat stopped at St. Helena, and our attendant took me a long walk to see Bonaparte behind a big, iron fence."

"And how did the banished emperor seem to you?"

"He was thinking too hard, as if it hurt him. My black man says he eats three sheep every day, and all the little children he can lay his hands on, but I don't believe it. He wasn't fierce, only sad."

The doctor turned to Mrs. Ritchie. "Don't be afraid, madam," he said. "Your nephew has a large head, but there is a great deal in it." He shook hands with Billy, as one man to another.

Aunt Ritchie was satisfied. Her motherly nature had to be sure there was nothing wrong with the little boy, and the doctor's complimentary words pleased her. William, holding her hand as they went back to the others, felt she was very like his mother: not so beautiful, perhaps, but with the same power to comfort, and to give you a feeling of peace. Besides this, Aunt Ritchie was humorous and laughed more easily than his mother. She read a comical fairy story to Richmond and him that night before they went to sleep, and she seemed to enjoy it as much as they did, and she nearly forgot to tell them to say their prayers.

The next day they went to St. James Park, very green and shady, with a pond where boys were sailing boats, and benches where nursemaids sat caring for babies. It was good to run on the green and then stretch out, panting, to watch the carriage wheels rumble by in the road, or the horsemen gallop past at high speed, leaving a fine dust of gravel scattered on both sides.

And the following day Mrs. Ritchie took the boys to Chiswick Mall, where William's great-uncle and aunt, Dr. and

Mrs. Turner, kept a school for boys. The Turners were a respectable, middle-aged couple who lived as much in the past as the yellow, time-worn books packed around the walls of the doctor's study, a dim little room off the main entrance. All you could see was a pair of broad shoulders behind the desk.

"Well, well." The huge man adjusted his gold-rimmed spectacles and peered at William when he and Richmond came in. "So you're Anne Becher's son. 'Miss Nancy' she used to be called. It was always 'Miss Nancy' and 'Miss Harriet' with your great-grandmother and great-aunt Becher, even when your mother and her sister came there as little girls."

"Dr. Turner!" his wife interrupted, entering the study. "How do you do, boys?" she greeted them briefly. She was a dried-up little woman with two deep wrinkles between her eyebrows from long frowning over account-books. "The Warings' bill is way past due," she said anxiously, showing her husband the sheet.

"So it is." Dr. Turner looked over the bill. "I must do something about that," he said vaguely. "I was just thinking about Miss Nancy. Wasn't she the prettiest child you ever saw, Mrs. Turner?"

"Yes, indeed." His wife nodded vigorously.

"Is your mother still so pretty? Speak up, my boy."

"Mamma is a beautiful lady," William didn't hesitate to say.

"Ah, yes, I remember she was a beauty ten years ago at the Bath Assembly balls the last time we were there," the big man smiled. He turned to other subjects. Did William know his alphabet? Could he write? Would he like to meet the pupils at Chiswick? It was time for recess.

So they all went into the courtyard where a game of cricket was going on. Those who were not playing stood on the sidelines and cheered for their comrades. A few boys were spinning tops, and some were amusing themselves with private races. Most of them were older than William and Richmond, but they welcomed the doctors' guests, and soon the two were joining in with one group or another.

They had lunch over much noisy talk and laughter in the dining hall. William thought he wouldn't mind going to school here, where there were so many good boys to play with. London would be a fine city to call your own, too.

But first he had to go to Fareham, where the Bechers were expecting him. The Indian attendant decided they must be getting on with the final lap of their journey.

"Let me stay here with you," William begged Aunt Ritchie. "I don't want to live in Fareham. I like your house better. And Rich is going to be here."

"Let Bill stay too, Aunt Ritchie," his cousin put in.

Their aunt laughed and put an arm around each of them. "I'd like to keep both of you," she admitted. "But the Bechers would not forgive me if I prevented you from going to Fareham, Billy. And Richmond will be going somewhere to school in the fall. Perhaps we can arrange to send you to the same place."

This was a comfort to both boys. Before William left he remembered a present he had brought for Mrs. Ritchie — a fine, white woolen shawl. "And I have one for great-grandmamma and Aunt Becher." He showed them off proudly.

Aunt Ritchie was delighted with the present. She put it around her shoulders with a grand air, declaring she would wear it to the play that very night, even though the weather was quite warm. The Indian came in just then to tell William they must be on their way, and he found it very hard to say good-bye.

But eventually they were on the road, travelling in a post chaise to Southampton, seventy-nine miles southwest of London, and from there along the coast to Fareham, the tiny sea-swept village where the Bechers lived. As they entered the main cobblestone street, the chimes were ringing softly in the spire of the village church, like a benediction on the neat, white stone cottages clustered beneath. It was a peaceful sound, and Fareham was like a storybook town, William thought, with its sea breeze, its bright, washed look, and the sight of the uniformed officers here and there along the streets. Fareham was peopled mostly by the officers and by resolute old ladies who saw their sons and grandsons go off to sea, to battle and to settle colonies, perhaps never to return. These grandams waited patiently for what might happen, kept house, gossipped with their neighbors, and played whist every night as if it were the only thing in the world that mattered. And the younger women, daughters, sweethearts, wives who stayed behind, learned to follow the traditional spirit of the seafarer's family, a cheerful acceptance of fate.

Two such women were the Bechers, mother and daughter, whose house had stood in the middle of the village for many years, like a sentinel with its roof rising above the others, a sort of landmark among the watchers of the sea. Its quaint garden was chock full of flowers that sunshiny day in June, neat patterns of brilliant bloom that sent forth a pungent fragrance as William and the attendant went up the walk toward the doorway.

Inside, the house was almost as fragrant as out, with the spiciness of potpourri filling the wide, shallow hall into which they stepped. A pleasant housekeeper by the name of Anna, who had opened the door, showed them into the parlour where the Bechers were waiting.

"Your humble servant presents Master Thackeray." The

Indian bowed to the two ladies, while Aunt Becher, with a squeak of delight, ran forward to greet William. "Miss Nancy's child, come to us at last!" She put her arms around him. "Haven't you got a kiss for your Aunt Becher, William?"

She was a small, spry, friendly woman of forty-odd, with two red spots of perpetual excitement burning in her cheeks. William kissed her, explaining, "That's from Mamma. She told me to kiss you for her." He didn't want them to think he went around kissing everybody of his own accord. But Aunt Becher gave him another squeeze.

"Well, Miss Becher," her mother said finally, a touch of vinegar in her voice, "don't you think it is about time the boy's great-grandmama got a look at him?"

Aunt Becher stood aside, murmuring, "Of course, Mamma," and William stared hard at the picturesque old lady who came toward him slowly, leaning on a long, tortoise-shell cane. She was about eighty years of age, with a little puff of snow-white hair under her cap, and a pair of bright blue eyes. Her dignified dress nearly touched the floor, but just beneath it he noticed the prettiest little black velvet slippers with high heels. She held out a bony hand laden with a good many rings. "Shake hands with your great-grandmamma, William."

He remembered his mother's instructions, and as he took her fingers, he reached up on tiptoe. "Mamma said I must kiss you, too."

The old lady's sharp eyes twinkled. "Very well, let's get it over with quickly." She bent her cheek to him. She didn't hold much with kissing.

His uncle Charles Becher, who happened to be visiting at Fareham, came in just as William finished, and offered another family kiss, but the boy shook his head. "I only take those from ladies."

Uncle Charles, who looked like William's mother, but was plumper and not at all beautiful, threw back his head and roared. "You're right, too, my lad, quite right."

Before they had tea, Mrs. Becher, taking her great-grandson's hand, led him around before the family portraits that lined the walls of the low-pitched parlour. Nearly all of them had been naval lieutenants or captains; one had been painted by Sir Joshua Reynolds — Mrs. Becher, tapping the frames with her tortoise-shell cane as she went along, lingered proudly over the signature of the famous artist. "And here is your mother's father," she stopped before the picture above the mantelpiece. "My son, John Harman Becher, God rest his soul."

William, gazing up at his grandfather's face, found it very familiar. There were his mother's large, blue-grey eyes, her fine nose, and full mouth. But the young man in the picture, stylish in a red coat and lace ruffles, looked arrogant — too fine, too proud, William thought, not sweet like his mother. He had examined all the paintings with unusual interest for a six-year-old. He liked to draw — at home he was always making pictures — and the idea of all these great drawings of his ancestors appealed to him immensely. He stood with his hands behind his back, his legs spread slightly apart, looking around from one to another.

And after tea, when the Bechers began to ask him questions about India, his home at Alipur and its surroundings, he suddenly asked for pencil and paper. "I can show you better the way it was if I draw it," he explained. Aunt Becher was only too glad to supply the materials, and William sketched the house clearly and accurately, including Betty at the top drying towels, and Jocko peeking out of the window. He drew palm trees and little hills and a walk to represent the terrace. The Indian, who stood in back of him, grinned broadly as the picture grew. "It is exact," he told the Bechers.

Aunt Becher and her mother were amazed at the talent William showed. "Do you take lessons in art?" his aunt asked him.

"Oh, no, I just draw. I like to do it." The portraits inspired him to untried fields, and he lined a little sketch of his great-grandmother, her puff of hair and an elongated cane. There was a hint of exaggeration that made them laugh. "The boy not only has talent," Uncle Charles observed, "but humour as well."

William enjoyed being at Fareham. He cried some when the faithful Indian attendant finally returned to Calcutta. If he, Billy, could only have gone along, to see his mother again! But Aunt Becher took him to the meadow and showed him how to make cowslip-balls, and in the berry patch which stretched below the garden to the river, she let him eat all the raspberries he wanted, and he soon forgot his sorrow. He was always to remember his great-aunt's kindness to him, and a long time afterward Miss Becher turned up only slightly disguised as Miss Martha Honeyman in William's novel, "The Newcomes." His new life was making a lasting impression on him.

He slept in the children's room of the house ("the upper room"), in the same little white bed — the first in a row of four — that his mother had used. And he was given the same willow plates for his own at table (there was cherry pie every Sunday!), and the same little pair of pattens to wear when the rain swept along the sea wall and down into the village.

And if his Aunt Becher was strict in some of her ways, trying to make him remember not to run up and down the carved staircase by having him sit on a chair for fifteen

minutes; if she sent him to his room for overturning the jar
of potpourri while he was chasing the cat; if she denied him
dessert for three nights because he stole the plate of raspberry tarts from the cook's pantry, she and his great-grandmother were nevertheless good to him. And his Uncle
Charles was a good sort.

Yes, William was quite content at Fareham. When fall
came, he wished they had not decided to send him to boarding school in Southampton.

3

A Cruel Boarding School

THE DAMP, musty-smelling, ramshackle institution which Mr. and Mrs. Arthur of Southampton called their boarding school for boys, had an excellent reputation among parents who had done no more than read its circulars, written by its oily-mouthed proprietor.

But William could sense from the dismal entryway, devoid of light and any sort of welcome save the cheerless odor of stale cabbage, that the Arthurs' school was going to be an evil place to live. A chill to match the unheated corridor went down his small spine as he and Anna approached the schoolmaster's parlour.

Not that the mealy-mouthed Mr. Arthur, a wizened man of fifty, in dull, stained breeches and spotted waistcoat, didn't fill Anna's ears with fine phrases about his happiness in receiving her charge, Master Thackeray. The proprietor rubbed his hands and smiled craftily as he spoke, his beady black eyes gleaming, his tousled black hair threatening to fall across them every second, when he would thrust it back with a nervous gesture of irritation. "You may tell your mistress the young man will get the best of care here, the best of care. Plenty of food — we always buy the best, though it costs more — good beds, plenty of exercise, Latin, geography and ciphering." He pushed back a lock of hair. "Of course, we don't believe in spoiling the boys." He picked up a cane lying across his desk. " 'Spare the rod and spoil the child,' you know." His thin lips pressed together tightly.

Anna had been brought up by that rule, but William had

become a favorite with her, and she considered him a good child. "You'll not need it often with Master William," she snapped. "He's a good boy."

"Of course, of course. We shall be able to judge when he needs caning, however. And now you will be shown to your dormer, Master William." He rang a bell on his desk, and Mrs. Arthur came in from between the curtains which led to the rest of the apartment.

She was a blowsy woman, bigger than her husband, but from the expression on her doughy face it was not hard to see that she was completely cowed by the ugly little man. She was used to taking orders from him unquestioningly, for when he commanded, scarcely looking at her: "This is Master Thackeray, Fareham, Hampshire. Show him to the west dormitory and arrange for his trunk to be brought up," she turned silently and led the way out of the study, shuffling down the long, dark hall to the stairway.

William, clinging tightly to Anna's hand, followed with a sinking heart. The narrow sleeping room which they entered at the top of the stairs contained nothing but six cots stretched along one wall, and two shabby bureaus side by side along the other. Otherwise it was bare and cold, not even a carpet to take the chill from the floor. A sooty fireplace, grey with the scattered ashes of a fire long since forgotten, yawned drearily at the far end of the room, a symbol of the general gloominess of the school.

In spite of this, William felt a sudden rush of gladness as he stepped in, when the boy putting his things away in one of the bureaus turned his dark head toward the newcomers. "Rich!" "Bill!" The two cousins ran to meet each other. "I was afraid you wouldn't come," Richmond said. And William, "I was afraid you wouldn't be here. When did you come?" They both spoke at once.

Richmond explained that he and his brother George, who had been sent from India on the next boat, had arrived only that morning. "I wanted George to be in here with me, but they put him in the next room," he lamented.

"Mr. Arthur never allows brothers to stay together. They are a bad influence on each other," Mrs. Arthur repeated her husband's belief dully. She wondered about letting Richmond and William remain together, but decided that since they were only cousins, it could do no harm. She assigned the second bed and the drawer above Richmond's to William. When his trunk came up, Anna helped him put in the clothes and belongings he would use most, and the trunk was shoved under his cot, following instructions from Mrs. Arthur.

Downstairs somewhat later, the boys found the rest of the boarding pupils lounging in an empty classroom, in the awkward state of becoming acquainted. A few, who had been to the school before, talked idly among themselves; the rest gaped frankly at each other, trying to size up various possibilities. George Shakespear, a year or two older than his brother and cousin, came up to them as soon as he saw them. He was glad to see William, but after he had said hello, he scowled, "Pretty rum place, isn't it? How is your room?"

They compared notes, discovering the same comfortless atmosphere. And the gloom of the place did not lift. To William it was all strange and rather frightening. He understood only vaguely what Mr. Arthur told the group about their studies, their duties, their privileges, if such these could be called. But when a little fellow in the front row whispered to his neighbor during the schoolmaster's speech, and instantly received a clout on the side of his face with the man's cane, William knew the school was run by a tyrant. The boys all felt his cruelty. They were completely silent, but resentful, during the rest of his talk.

Dinner was eaten in the same sulky silence, with further cause: the food was scarce, and poorly cooked. A thin gruel, burnt potatoes, and a small piece of tough beef was all that was allotted to each boy, along with a single slice of bread. No one dared ask for more if he had wanted it, for fear of the cane hooked over the back of Mr. Arthur's chair, ready for use. After a gooey pudding for dessert, they left the table, still hungry and slightly sick. William, remembering Aunt Becher's tender, brown veal cutlets and the pies or tarts they had nearly every night at Fareham, was ready to run away that very night.

He and Richmond undressed and were ready for bed by the time Mrs. Arthur came to put out the candles, but they sat whispering a while with the rest of their schoolmates after she had gone down. George crept in from the next room and flung himself on William's bed. "Awful beast, isn't he?" He didn't have to tell the boys who he meant. They nodded in the darkness. "I'm going to write Papa. Maybe he'll take us away from here."

William and Richmond ardently hoped Mr. Shakespear would do so. Before he went to sleep, William knelt unhappily by his bed. If only he could have a good dream, and forget this horrible place!

The nightmare of William's first school grew worse as the weeks went by. There was rarely a fire in the dormitory, even on the rawest days. It was painful to have to leave a warm bed in the morning and dress in the icy darkness. The little boys shivered and shook, and sometimes one of them would sneak back to bed, only to be routed out later by Mr. Arthur with a few sound whacks of his cane. The pupils all suffered from chilblains and colds. The food did not improve. It became, if possible, less appetizing as the term progressed. The butter was often rancid; the meat had a putrid taste. The worst of it was that the boys couldn't write home and complain. All letters were dictated by Mrs. Arthur.

But one day Mr. Shakespear came to visit his sons, and, like most fathers, he took them along with their cousin to the best Southampton inn to dine. How good the beefsteak, hot rolls, tarts and fresh milk tasted to William, George and Richmond! They ate like three young wolves, until Mr. Shakespear laughingly protested they would eat themselves sick. "One would think the Arthurs never fed you," he commented.

The three looked at each other, and decided to tell him what the boarding school was like. Mr. Shakespear was very grave when they finished. He could not take the boys out of school until the term was finished — he had no home for them, had to go back to India in a month — but he would speak to the schoolmaster about food and conditions. In the meantime, he promised that he would take them out to dine often and William should go every time George and Richmond did. He gave his nephew a stack of pretty picture books to read.

For a short while after Mr. Shakespear made his complaint, conditions at the school were better. The quality of the food was not quite as bad as it had been, and now and then a skimpy fire took some of the chill from the dormitory. But the improvement didn't last long after William's uncle returned to India. Then the boys suffered as much as before. The only bright spot in William's life was the news which came from Calcutta around the middle of the year: his mother had married Captain Carmichael-Smyth, and they were eventually coming to England to live! Every week after that he expected his mother and his new "papa" to arrive, but "eventually" was a very long time, he discovered. The dreary life continued, the geography and arithmetic lessons in chilly classrooms; the poor food in the damp dining room, steamy from the kitchen, yet not really warm; the icy dressing and undressing in the dorm; the awful caning.

Then suddenly it was over. He caught a terrible cold which stubbornly resisted doctoring, and they sent him home to Fareham. It took only a single glance of inspection on the part of Miss Becher and her mother to realize what the school in Southampton must be like. William's thin body, his cough, his listless eyes told them enough, before he added to the testimony with stories that were shocking.

Aunt Becher was highly indignant. "You certainly shan't return to that miserable place! And I shall see what can be done to punish the tyrant who runs it." The red spots in her cheeks flamed with anger.

William's heart sang for joy. That night he slept an untroubled sleep in spite of his cough, the first he had had since he went to Southampton. Some weeks later when he had recovered and the weather had become warm, so that he could play out again and splash in the sea, he wrote happily to his mother:

My dearest of all mamas,
     I have much pleasure in writing you again from Fareham, to tell you how happy I am. . . . I saw a bird's nest with young ones in it, and a beautiful honeysuccle bush, and the Robbins in another place. This has been Neptune day with me: I call it so, because I go into the water and am like Neptune. Your old acquaintances are very kind to me, and give me a great many cakes and a great many kisses.
     . . . I am grown a great boy; I am three feet eleven inches high. . . . I shall go on Monday to Chiswick and hear the boys speak; I intend to be one of those heroes in time. . . .
I have lost my cough, and am quite well, strong, saucy and

hearty, and can eat grandmama's gooseberry pyes famously, after which I drink yours and my papa's good health and speedy return.

If their return would come true, William could ask for nothing more. Just to be at Fareham made him feel contented again. On Miss Becher's recommendation, George and Richmond were sent back to Aunt Ritchie's. The school at Southampton became only a bad dream.

4

Chiswick Mall

IN THE AUTUMN it was decided that William should go to
Dr. Turner's school in Chiswick Mall. He was taken up
to London for the Speech Day exercises, where the sight of
those "good boys" he had liked when he was there before,
and the sound of their oratory made him wish to be a hero,
too. He became a pupil at the beginning of the new term.

The school was in Walpole House, which seemed larger
and more impressive as he went through the wrought-iron
gate with Uncle Charles than it had when he went there
with Aunt Ritchie. Maybe that was because he was going
to be a boarder now, and he was a little scared. After his experience at Southampton, he preferred Fareham to any
school life.

The portly doctor and his wife tried to treat William more
like a relative than a student. They often had him in their
own parlor, where he played with their two small daughters,
or they would invite him to take tea with them instead of in
hall with the rest.

Their efforts only made him feel uncomfortable, however.
For one thing, the tremendous size of his great-uncle filled
him with fearful awe, and he was usually at a loss to answer
the prying questions boomed at him during these visits.
When Dr. Turner would inquire in his stentorian voice,
"Well, lad, when is your mother coming from India with her
new husband?" William could only stutter, "I don't know,
sir," and long for the day when his mother would finally
be in England.

His being the schoolmaster's nephew set him apart from the other boys, too. They thought it wiser not to let him in on any plans because his uncle might make him tell. An inmate of the doctor's parlor was regarded with suspicion. Even in chapel, where he joined in the giggling and arm-pinching that went on as the doctor read services for two hours morning and evening, William had no special friend to sit with and share intimately the undercover activity. The Shakespear boys, to his disappointment, had gone to a different school, and he was slow to make friends.

Between the boys' coolness of attitude and the doctor's formidable presence in the drawing room, the first term was a lonely one for William. His only fun came in occasional visits to the Ritchies', where he would sometimes find George and Richmond as well. There was a new baby at his aunt's, a little girl named Charlotte, and William Ritchie was already running around the nursery, getting his cousins to go down on all fours and ride him on their backs, or help sail his boats in St. James pond.

Aunt Ritchie never asked her nephews embarrassing questions. She laughed with them, entertained them, saw that they ate a good hearty dinner and tea, and treated them like people, not like annoying charges. Monday morning at Walpole House was especially dull after Billy had been to the Ritchies'.

The second term was better. He was used to the routine at Walpole House, he didn't mind his uncle's questions so much, and the boys sometimes let him in on their pranks. Two of his Thackeray relatives, Uncle Thomas and Uncle Francis, had him to visit. Uncle Francis, along with Mr. Langslow, a family friend who was married to Sarah Jane Thackeray, were in charge of William's inheritance from his father. Mr. Langslow was considered his guardian.

It was this gentleman who came driving up to Walpole

House one evening just after tea in his smart equipage with brass-studded harness. A number of boys were watching him from the bow window of the upstairs hall, where they usually loitered on the way to their rooms. An outsider coming to the school at this hour aroused their curiosity.

"I say, Bill, isn't that your guardian?" asked a fat boy near the front.

William squinted to get a better look — he was a little nearsighted — and pressed close to the window. "It is! It's Mr. Langslow!" he shouted, and tore down the steps without waiting to be summoned. He thought he knew why his guardian had come. His mother had written some months before that she and Captain Carmichael-Smyth were leaving India on the next boat. Surely his guardian must have some word or he wouldn't have come. Trembling with excitement, Billy opened the study door.

"Ah, William," Dr. Turner said, "I was just going to send for you. Mr. Langslow has good news for you."

"Is my mother — ?"

"She arrived in Chatham this afternoon," his guardian said, as if it were nothing unusual, as if it had been five minutes instead of two years since Billy had seen his mother. "I'm going to take you to her."

"I'll get my things." William was ready to leave on the run.

"Not so fast, young man." Mr. Langslow stopped him. "We shan't be starting till morning." William's woebegone look brought a word of kindly reassurance. "Don't worry, I promise you we'll leave early. At dawn if you like."

It was hard to sleep that night, and Billy was awake before sunrise, impatiently waiting for Mr. Langslow to fetch him. But as the first streaks of light shone in the sky they were bowling over the road to Chatham, and before noon they drew up in front of the inn where Captain and Mrs. Carmichael-Smyth were staying. Billy's heart was beating wildly as the landlord led him up to their rooms.

The next thing he knew he was in his mother's arms, and she was saying "Billy-boy!" and crying and hugging him very close. He kissed her a great many times, until at last she laughed in a trembly sort of way. "Billy, you'll smother me in a moment! And you haven't said a word to me yet."

Even then he couldn't speak. He just stood looking at her. She was very beautiful, more beautiful than he had remembered. Her great eyes were so velvety, her dark hair so shining, and her skin so soft and white, like a lily petal. He kissed her cheek again.

She put him gently from her, and gave her hand to Mr. Langslow. "I had no idea the child would be so moved," he heard her say. Then Captain Carmichael-Smyth caught him by the shoulders and turned him round. "Well, Billy-boy, how about a greeting for your old playmate — and new papa?"

"Hello . . . Papa." William grinned. The Captain, still splendid-looking in his loose, grey uniform of the East India service, with all his medals, was a very good fellow. "Want to ride me on your shoulders, sir?"

"Not a great boy like you!" The Captain protested, and Billy's mother, hearing this, had to measure her son's height, and soon he was telling her about Chiswick, the boys there, the Turners, the Ritchies, and the Bechers, and it was as if she had always been in England. He talked happily all day — he had never been so happy before.

The Carmichael-Smyths accompanied him back to Chiswick. His mother was pleased with the way the Turners handled Walpole House. "I don't think there could be a better school for young boys," she said. And mother-like she was more than pleased to find out that William stood sixth in the school, though of the twenty-six pupils only four were older than he. "I'm proud of you, Billy," she beamed with a loving smile.

He was eager for praise, he had missed it so long. "I'm going to fag hard till midsummer; then maybe I'll get a medal!" he bragged. Then he showed her his books, and she noticed nearly all the pages were decorated with drawings of some sort — funny little designs, droll faces, cleverly distorted figures. "You seem to practise your drawing lessons all over," she remarked. "You have certainly developed your talent. Who teaches you here?"

"Nobody. I just draw for fun." He showed her stacks of papers he had in his room — knights in armor, soldiers with great shields, fierce dragons, demons — all the things he read about in stories.

"Why, these are splendid!" His mother leafed through them with growing admiration. "I must write your Aunt Harriet Graham of your talent."

William remembered his little cousin. "How is Polly?" he wanted to know.

"She is well, and growing very fast, almost as tall as you. We call her Mary now. We never use her nickname any more."

"Polly is nicer," William said. "I'm always going to call her that."

His mother laughed at him, and gave him a guinea to spend. A whole guinea! Now he could buy something for all the fellows. He left her to look over his drawings, and went to seek out his little circle. By nightfall the guinea had been spent in presents for each of them, and his mother, though she was glad to learn of his generosity, was alarmed that he was such a spendthrift. She decided to keep the sovereign and six shillings his Aunt Graham and Polly had sent to him, and give him the money a little at a time.

The remaining days at Chiswick were tranquil ones. At school he spent a good deal of his time painting the scenes for a toy theatre one of the boys started. He saw his parents every few weeks, and that summer they were all together with the Bechers at Fareham.

Certainly there was never a kinder stepfather than the Captain. He knew Billy's love for adventure stories, and one day he gave him "The Scottish Chiefs" to read. "But don't let your mother see it," he advised. "I've an idea she'd think you were a bit too young for novels. But I read 'em when I was your age."

They exchanged a wink. Billy carried the book to the summerhouse that afternoon, where he lay on his stomach, listening to the church bells ringing for King George's coronation, and devouring his first novel. He read all afternoon without stopping. He was so entranced with the story, he had to see what happened to the hero, Wallace. He took one or two peeks at the last chapter: poor Wallace was to die. As he read closer and closer to the sad ending, he could not read the words for his tears. He closed the book. He did not care to finish, but he felt wonderful, elated somehow, instead of sad — as if he had lived through a magnificent experience. From now on, he would read all the novels he could find.

When his final Speech Day at Chiswick arrived two years later, his parents were both on hand to hear him deliver Hannibal's address to his soldiers. As his young, clear voice rang out (after the opening lines, he had stopped trembling, and spoke easily), his mother thought she was going to break down. She was sure there was no pupil equal to her son.

5

First Days At Charterhouse

CHARTERHOUSE SCHOOL, Smithfield, was one of the great public schools in England. It and the Merchant Taylor's School, which adjoined it on Charterhouse Square, had been founded in the fourteenth century by two of the leading City Companies or corporations running the trade of London. This was the only sense in which the schools were public, for the fees were high, and only the sons of gentlemen and titled families attended.

Just now, the fees at Charterhouse were somewhat lower, because of the new Madras method which Dr. Russell, the Head, had installed. Under this system, the older boys were put in charge of teaching and disciplining the younger, and less than half the number of masters were needed, which cut the rates considerably. A good many East India families were sending their sons there for this reason, and William's parents, whose means were comfortable but moderate, decided it was the best school they could find to follow his education at Chiswick.

He entered its hallowed halls in January, 1822, overwhelmed by the enormous number of pupils and the noise they made. Big boys, little boys, fat boys, thin boys; handsome ones, ugly ones, fair ones, dark ones — four hundred and eighty of them, crowding the Green, the halls, the Square. In Southampton there had been only a handful, and at Chiswick, twenty-six. He felt as if he were in the middle of a seething, shouting mob, ready to bear down on him any moment.

His first interview with the Headmaster was far from reassuring. Dr. Russell, his shaggy, black brows and beak-like nose giving him the appearance of a ferocious eagle as he sat in his don's robe with its wide sleeves, shot his questions at the boy in a loud, harsh voice. "Construe the Latin verb, 'to be.'" "Where is Madagascar?" "Where is Mexico?" They came hurtling at William one after another like cannon balls. Left alone, with plenty of time, he could have answered them all. He liked to fit his textbook knowledge in with his daydreams, but now all he could say was, "I can't think of it, sir," or stutter some incorrect reply.

"I'm afraid you have been an idle pupil," the Doctor concluded. "You will learn to mend your ways at Charterhouse." He summoned a porter, and commanded in a thundering voice: "Take that boy and his box to the matron, and make my compliments to the junior master. Tell him the boy knows nothing and will just do for the lowest form."

The lowest form! It was unfair, humiliating. William wanted to protest, but he would as soon have stuck his head into a lion's mouth; a lion, in fact, would be less fearsome than Dr. Russell. Though his face was burning with shame and anger, he scurried out after the porter, relieved at least that the interview was over.

The Reverend Edward Penny was the junior master at whose house in Wilderness Row, Clerkenwell, William was to board — Penny's house, the boys called it. The master had a coarse-grained face lit up by a bulbous red nose extending beyond his thick mouth. He found small boys among the world's most annoying creatures, and to have fifty of them jammed in his house this year was a severe trial to his patience. He thrust William into a dormitory with ten others, and left him to shift for himself.

The boys were busy swapping stories and treasures of the

Christmas holiday just passed, but they were never too busy to examine a newcomer with the regular questions: "What's your name?" "How old are you?" "Who's your father?" "How much money have you got?"

In answer to the last, William dug down among the jingle of coins in the pocket of his sailor suit. His mother had given him five shillings before he left; Aunt Becher, one shilling threepence; Aunt Ritchie, five shillings; Uncle Francis and Mr. Langslow, half a crown each; and his step-father, most generous of all, had presented him with a gold sovereign. He had a feeling, from the critical eyes surrounding him, that the sovereign would bring him respect if nothing else did. There it was, shining among the handful of money pieces he pulled out.

His schoolfellows were only mildly impressed. Some of

them had received twice as much from visiting relatives at Christmas. Still, a sovereign for a ten-year-old wasn't bad — a good source for a loan if your own ran out.

"Nice tip." A huge, surly-faced boy, with exceptionally large hands and feet, picked up the sovereign. "Who gave it to you?"

"My stepfather."

The boy tossed the goldpiece up and caught it as William watched apprehensively. Then he made a move to put it in his pocket. "I'll keep it for you, Thackeray. You'll spend it all at once."

"No, I won't." William reached for the piece. "Give me my sovereign."

The other held it high above his head. "Jump!" he challenged. "If you touch it you can have it." But he closed his fist over the coin so that William couldn't actually touch it even though he tapped his tormentor's fingers. After several trials, he gave up scornfully. "You're cheating. You know I can't touch it." His accusation brought the bully's hand full in William's face with a resounding slap, while the sovereign went clattering to the floor.

"Cheating, am I? There goes your old sovereign. Pick it up, pick it up!" roared the offender, Tom Creighton.

Stunned by the surprise slap, and squinting with his usual nearsightedness, William bent over to grope for the coin, which had rolled some distance along the floor. A second later, he felt the sharp toe of Tom's boot in the seat of his trousers, and went sprawling to the floor, with the hoots and jeers of the onlookers pounding in his ears.

Hot, salty drops stung his eyelids, but he kept them from spilling over, found his sovereign, and pocketed it quietly as he stumbled up. After this, he wouldn't be so quick to display his wealth. What an unkind welcome to give a new pupil! He looked around for a sympathetic expression, but most of the boys had already dismissed the incident. Creighton was an acknowledged bully, and while few really liked him, his power was unquestioned, and everyone had to be initiated to his brutality some time; Thackeray might as well get used to it at once. Had one of them bothered to explain this to William, he might not have felt so lost, but as he watched them returning to their former groups, bickering over their bargains, bursting into a roar of laughter at some whispered joke, he wondered whether he would ever find a friend among them.

The whole school seemed crude to him. There were no comforts, no niceties of a home. In the morning, you had to wash outside the house under the cistern, pushing for a place at the leaden trough that served as a bowl among the other forty-nine crowding it. William would just as soon not wash at all — the water was like ice, the strong soap burned his face, and the sight of slimy yellow lumps of it floating around in the trough made him a little sick — but he couldn't sneak out of it, because the *praepositus* (Dr. Russell had given the student masters this high-sounding Latin title) stood by with a cane, ready to whack all dodgers.

After a simple breakfast served on a bare, wooden table, the boys were lined up and marched through a tunnel under the street to the school. By the end of a week, William was running back and forth through this tunnel like the rest of them, but the first day it appeared dark and menacing. He didn't know where they were going, and when the horse's hooves pounded on the pavement overhead, he was sure the top was going to cave in. He was shaking with terror by the time they came up some steps and onto the Green, or playground of the school.

Never was a quadrangle more misnamed, for not a spot of

SCHOOL DAYS

green showed anywhere in the barren yard. The grass had long since been trampled out by the feet of fighting, playing, running boys, and there were no trees save two blackened stumps, nor any beds where flowers might be expected to brighten the view when summer came. Near the south side of the iron fence stood a small, wooden platform, with three steps leading up to it.

"What is that?" William nudged the boy beside him.

"What's what? — Oh, you mean the Block!" his partner said carelessly.

"What do they use it for?" It was all so puzzling.

"You'll find out soon enough." The other wagged his head with a knowing air.

If only they would tell him things, William thought, it wouldn't be so hard. He felt all at sea. Before class the boys marched to Chapel, most ancient among Charterhouse buildings. Here was the Founder's Tomb, ornamented with strange carvings that seemed to take on life in the cobwebby patterns of light falling through the old Gothic panes. As Dr. Russell thundered at the rows of boys before him, William's mind wandered in a maze of dreams about the figures on the Tomb. If he had a pencil, he would sketch them, but as it was, he let his imagination run riot until he almost shut out the Doctor's awful tones. On the other side of the chapel sat the "Codds," the old pensioners whom the school supported, and he could hear them cough apologetically now and then, but, as with the headmaster and the other boys, William was only half aware of their presence.

In the midst of this blissful meandering through the world of fancy, he suddenly felt a stap of sharp pain in his leg: his partner had kicked him in the shin. "Owoo!" He was so startled the cry came out before he knew it, and the mischief was done.

Dr. Russell stopped speaking, and fixed him with a terrible eye. A monitor came hurrying down the aisle. "What is the disturbance?" he demanded in a stage whisper.

"Please, sir, he kicked me."

"Never mind. You shouldn't have cried out like that. I will see you at the Block after service."

Quiet was restored at the expense of many giggles hastily smothered throughout the chapel, and the rest of the service was a nightmare to William. As soon as it was over, the monitor collared him, and led him to the Block in the Green. He was pushed up the three steps, onto the platform, and whack! whack! whack-whack-whack he was caned five times for creating a disturbance in Chapel. When it was over, he fled to the farthest corner of the Green, smarting with pain and shame. As he stood there with his hands covering his face, he felt a tug on the collar of his sailor suit, and turned to find the urchin who had kicked him.

"Now do you know what the Block is for?" he grinned.

William scowled at him. "You should have got the caning. You shouldn't have kicked me."

The other shrugged. "You shouldn't have howled. You'll learn. Anyhow, you got off easy — only five whacks with a cane. Look!" He pulled up his blouse and displayed red marks on his back. "That's what Dr. Russell does, with a *birch rod!* They're fading now," he added, straightening his blouse.

William learned a great deal in a short time. He schooled himself to stifle his cries the next time someone kicked his shin in Chapel. Instead, he kicked back with all his might, and the affair was at an end. During the rest of the service he day-dreamed in peace, gazed at the stone statue of Thomas Sutton in gown and ruff, and speculated on the various mis-fortunes that might have brought the old "Codds" back to

Charterhouse, their old school, to live here now on charity. He felt deeply sorry for the tottering men in their black gowns who went creeping along the ancient archways and cloisters like silhouettes of an age long past.

He learned to keep out of the formidable Dr. Russell's way as much as possible. Luckily, the doctor taught only the Upper Form, and while William was determined to rise from the lowest, he was just as glad to receive his lessons from a preapositus, or from Penny, who, more from laziness than anything else, was lax in matters of discipline. Not so the Doctor. Nearly every afternoon a batch of boys was led to the Block; an attendant held up a bundle of birch rods from which the Doctor chose a supple one. Then wh-ssh! wh-ssh! the blows fell. Afterwards, the boys would compare notes, counting the marks and the size of the welts to see who had received the worst whipping. They seemed to enjoy being able to boast the thickest welts, or the greatest number, but William found small comfort in such boasting. He preferred to avoid a trip to the Block whenever possible.

The games were the worst ordeal. Directly following classes every afternoon, the student body gathered on the Green en masse. The playground was packed, the noise so deafening William had to put his hands over his ears. The Upper Form monitors organized cricket matches between teams chosen from each form, and William had the misfortune to be chosen the first day. His nearsightedness kept him from seeing the ball when he came to bat. His swing was wild — once, twice, three times he swung and missed.

The insults were merciless. "Take him away! Hang 'im!" "Look at the pirouette — what is this, a ballet?" He had to smile at the last jibe; he had swung so far around it must indeed have looked like a ballet dancer doing a fancy turn. He felt very foolish. "I can't see the ball coming," he

mumbled. But to his hardhearted schoolmates this was a
poor excuse.

When he did occasionally hit the ball, he was not much
better at running. He rarely reached safety, and he was
always put out. He longed to be excused from the games;
they caused him greater mortification than the whipping-
block, which was shared misery. As a poor athlete, he stood
almost alone.

He was beginning to think he couldn't stand to stay at
Charterhouse, when he found a source of solace. Toward the
end of the week, he noticed a small group making for the
gate leading from the Green, escaping stealthily from the
din. Out of curiosity he followed, and around the corner
he beheld an enchanting sight — a pastrycook's shop! A
tempting row of raspberry tarts was displayed in the window,
and the plump little mistress of the place was already reach-
ing in for six of them to sell to her band of customers. He
hurried in lest all of them should be sold before he could
buy one.

"Six, please," he told the pastrycook anxiously. He pulled
out half a crown. He could hardly wait till she brought
them.

Oh, the magical flavor of that first, fresh raspberry tart! Not even the sugar-coated cottage in "Hansel and Gretel" could have matched it. He munched it slowly, savoring every crumb.

"Good, aren't they?"

He wasn't aware till then that a boy about his size had been watching him, a bright-eyed boy with an open, attractive face, and an abundance of bright, brown hair. William's mouth was crammed full, so for the moment he could only assent, "Mmm-hm!" Then, swallowing, he offered, "Have one." The invitation was quickly accepted, and he observed, "I never knew there was a pastrycook's here."

"It takes awhile to find things out when you first come to a school." The other boy bit into his tart philosophically. "You're the new boy in the Tenth, aren't you?"

William nodded. "I'm supposed to be in the Sixth or Seventh, though."

"Dr. Russell always puts new pupils in the Tenth — unless your parents tip him well. Then he tries to put you where you belong. What's your name?"

"Thackeray." William had learnt by now that Charterhouse boys used only their surnames. "What's yours?"

"Carne." Then, after a minute, "Joe Carne," a friendly gesture.

"Bill Thackeray." William followed suit with a grateful smile. "Do you come here often?"

"Everybody does, nearly every day after games," Carne said. "Only there's a great rush, and half the time the pastry's all gobbled up before Mistress Cheney can wait on you. If we can get away without being seen before games, we can buy what we like." A talkative boy, he rattled on. William had been in the habit of hurrying off through the tunnel to Penny's house as soon as the games were over, to avoid further ridicule for his part in them. He made no mention of this to Carne, but he suddenly felt lighthearted and gay. If the games could be avoided, they were not so dreadful. And what a perfect refuge a pastrycook's was!

"How much money have you got?" Carne asked the inevitable.

William produced the change from the half crown. He bought enough tarts for all around — the others were George Venables, Henry Liddell, and Walter Fawsett — and ginger-beer to wash down the pastry. He walked back to the Green arm in arm with Carne. He hardly realized he had spent one of his half crowns in a very short while. His stomach was pleasantly full of his favorite sweet. He had found a beautiful haven — and a friend.

6

A Disastrous Fight

ONCE HE HAD DISCOVERED this delightful retreat, William
made frequent trips to the pastrycook's. If Joseph Carne
didn't care to go with him, he went by himself. When he
felt particularly homesick, he bought more penny tarts than
usual. For instance, he spent a whole half crown on them
at a single session the day his mother wrote to say that she
and his stepfather could not "ask William out" (as the parents of pupils were allowed to do every three weeks) when
their turn next came. Her husband, promoted to Major,
had accepted a post at Addiscombe, and they would just be
getting settled. William had been marking the days off on
his calendar until then; it was a terrible disappointment!
He drank the final drop of gingerbeer his last penny had
bought, and heaved a disconsolate sigh.

"Are you ill, Master Thackeray?" The pastrycook knew
him well by now. "I told you not to eat so many tarts at
one time."

"It's not the tarts, Mrs. Cheney." He sighed again, put
down his mug, and wandered out of the shop. Even the
tinkle of the little bell as the door closed behind him
sounded dismal. It was a half-holiday, but it was raining,
and no one in his form had cared to go out, even for sweets.
He pulled his ulster close about him, and followed two
Upper Form pupils — Walter Fawsett's older brother,
(called Fawsett *major* while Walter was Fawsett *minor*) and
John Roupelle — back to the school. He kept a safe distance
behind them for he stood rather in awe of the Upper Form

boys. They were almost men: a good many of them smoked "seegars," and on some you could see the smudgy line of sprouting mustaches just above the upper lip.

But as they neared the edge of the Green, Roupelle happened to turn around. Spying William, he called out: "Step it up, Thackeray; we'll wait for you. We're going to the long-room."

He was monitor of the week at Penny's, so there was nothing William could do but obey. He quickened his pace until he had caught up with them, and they all descended into the tunnel together.

The long-room at Penny's served as a recreation ground in rainy weather when the boys could not play on the Green. It was a rectangular room used principally for lectures or classes that included all those who boarded at Penny's. There was a similar one at Reverend Churton's next door, and at Dr. Russell's house.

Today the long-room was overflowing. William was about to ease out of the door after Fawsett and Roupelle had joined a group of their fellows, when Carne, Venables, Fawsett minor and a boy by the name of Thomas Gossip hailed him. "Hi, Thackeray, come over!"

He went reluctantly, though he was glad they thought to seek his company. Perhaps they were beginning to regard him as a crony. He rather doubted this, however, as Joe Carne was the only one who treated him at all like a friend. At the moment he would have preferred being alone, or with some true intimate like Richmond. He wished ardently that Rich had come to Charterhouse instead of attending military school. With these uncertain feelings he approached his new companions, and it didn't make him any more at ease with them to have Gossip blurt out, "Venables says he can lick you, Thackeray."

"I did not!" George contradicted. "You asked me if I thought Thackeray could lick me, and I said no."

"It's the same thing." Gossip was anxious to engineer a fight. "Well, can you?" he demanded of William.

"I don't know." Although he wasn't exactly spoiling for battle, William didn't want to admit that he thought Venables might lick him, and it was just possible that he could defeat his opponent. They were about the same size.

"There's only one way to find out — we'll hold a boxing match right now." Gossip seized his opportunity. "I'll ask the monitor." And he was off in the direction of Roupelle, where they heard him petitioning: "I came to ask leave for Venables and Thackeray to fight, sir. Over there." He jabbed his thumb back toward the boys.

John Roupelle looked to his fellow-monitors, Dashwood Stettell, Robert Morris and George Cole, for advice. Matches were allowed between the Lower form pupils if they were supervised by a monitor.

"Let them fight it out, Roupelle," Dashwood said. "We've nothing else to do."

"Yes, we need some amusement on a rainy day like this," persuaded Morris. "Do give permission, Roupelle."

"Very well. Maybe Thackeray will turn out to be an expert, and thrash Venables. Come along." Gossip skipped ahead of them, pleased with himself at having arranged a fight. He passed the word around and within a few minutes the entire gathering had crowded into a ring at one end of the long-room. William chose Joe Carne as his bottle-holder, or second, while George Venables chose Walter Fawsett.

The backers were each given a bottle of cold water to administer to their contestants whenever treatment was needed. An area was marked off for the match, the boxers were shown to their corners, and Roupelle gave the signal to commence fighting. Without quite realizing how it happened, William was thrust into combat.

"Go it, Thackeray. Pitch into him!" shouted Joe, shoving his friend into the ring, while Fawsett urged, "Give it him, Venables!"

These cries were taken up by the spectators. "Go it, boys!" "Give it him, Venables; he can't fight!" "Two to one on young 'Thack'!" burst like noisy explosions from all over the audience.

William knew little of the art of fisticuffs, but he was suddenly imbued with fiery spirit, and ran forward to meet his opponent with both arms ready to hit out. He was surprised to find Venables' fist coming up between them and landing a sharp blow on his chin. Then another came quickly on his cheek, another on his chin, and he was down. (Cheers for Venables doubled.)

Carne came running to pick him up. "Give it him with your right," he whispered as he helped William get on his feet.

Reeling, and slightly dizzy, William plunged forward again. He managed to plant a blow full on his opponent's lower lip, which began to bleed. Then they were locked, and Roupelle had to pull them apart. As they came toward each other again, George Venables determined to return the cut on his lip, but his fist landed higher. William felt and heard a terrible *scrunch* of bone in his nose, and he was on the floor again with blood pouring from him.

Carne came running out again, this time to wash the victim with the water in his bottle. But the bleeding wouldn't stop, and William felt too faint to get up.

"On your feet, you coward; stand up and fight!" jeered Creighton, and two or three of his loyal subjects took it up feebly, but most of the boys realized from the loud crack that William's nose must be seriously injured. After a minute or two he did try to go on with the match, but the bleeding grew worse.

Creighton began to bellow again, but Roupelle silenced him sternly. "That will do, Creighton. Match postponed," he announced. "Go fetch the doctor," he directed Carne.

George Venables had grown quite pale at the sight of the damage he had done; he stood over William anxiously. "Sorry, old boy, didn't mean to break your nose," he murmured awkwardly. "Does it hurt much?"

"I can't tell," William said wonderingly. "I can't feel anything but a kind of pressing and lumpiness." He turned over the blood-soaked napkin Carne had applied, trying to find a dry spot. "I guess you win, Venables. You pitched into me, all right." He smiled feebly.

"Oh, no, it's a called match," George said quickly. "I am sorry about your nose, Bill."

"Never mind, George," William said gratefully. "Too bad it had to break up the fight." They both lamented the fact that theirs could not have become one of the historic battles of Charterhouse, one of those magnificent combats that lasted through ten, fifteen, a hundred rounds and ended only when one of the mighty went down like a felled tree, with impressive grandeur. "Ours was such a poor little two-penny affair. No one will ever remember this fight in years to come," William sighed.

"Except us," George amended.

"Except us," William smiled.

By the time the doctor arrived, they were the best of friends. It was Venables who, with Carne, helped William to his bed, where the physician applied cold compresses to the back of his neck, and examined the break in his nose.

"The bone has been split," the medical man told them. "But perhaps it will grow together again." He taped

William's nose so that if possible the two pieces would unite. It was a painful process, and the boy gritted his teeth and clung to Venables' arm till it was over. The bleeding had finally stopped, but he felt weak and sick to his stomach. His whole face was aching.

Within two or three days, however, the bones began to mend, and the aching lessened. Venables and Carne accompanied him everywhere, like a bodyguard. The three were an inseparable trio, sturdy Thackeray, with his large head and bandaged nose, walked between bright-eyed Carne and lean, serious-looking Venables. It was a friendship that mushroomed overnight as a result of the boxing match, but gave promise of becoming more durable as the three discovered further interests in common.

On the fourth afternoon, when the fight had become but a dim memory to most of the onlookers and William was beginning to feel the first sensations of itching that follow an injury of that sort, he was hurrying to meet his friends at Mrs. Cheney's. Mr. Brown, the math teacher, had kept him in a half an hour to make up work he had missed. He hoped the boys would still be at the pastrycook's when he got there. He was half-running, head bent, and so did not notice the hulking figure of Tom Creighton until it was upon him, blocking the path.

"Where do you think you're going in such a hurry?" demanded the bully.

"Mrs. Cheney's, to meet Carne and Venables. Get out of my way, Creighton."

Creighton was in the habit of giving orders and he did not enjoy receiving them, especially from William. "How much money have you got with you?"

"Five shillings, all I have left till I go home again."

"Well, loan it to me. I need it." Creighton held out his hand.

"I won't."

"Yes, you will, Thackeray." Creighton advanced menacingly. He happened to be in a tight fix. He had run up a bill — tick, the boys called it — at the pastrycook's himself, and had been refused any more credit. If he could pay something on his tick by intimidating Thackeray for a loan, he could get by until his next allowance came. But William stood his ground and refused obstinately. At last Creighton, in a fit of anger, let go with his fist flush on William's broken nose. "Very well, stingy. Take that!"

The pain was blinding. William staggered back, and sank in a heap as the blackness overcame him. Creighton, scared at the effect of his blow, was sneaking off the Green as William's two friends came in search of him.

"What happened?" George rushed up.

"Creighton," William managed to gasp as he reached for his handkerchief. His nose had begun to bleed again.

Joe ran after the bully and shook his fist. "You'll pay for this, Creighton. You hit Thackeray's broken nose."

"What if I did?" sneered Tom, who had become reassured at seeing William revive enough to speak. "He's a stingy-gut!" He walked off before the smaller boy could defend William further.

This time there was no hope of pulling the bridge of William's nose together. "It's hopelessly smashed," the doctor said. "I'm afraid you'll always have a flattened nose, my boy."

William was miserable with pain, which was worse than before. His head ached, too, and his soul longed for the comfort his mother would have given him — and a little, secretly, for revenge on Creighton. The bully had been whipped soundly at the Block for his crime, which soon became known to the headmaster through the physician, but one "operation" more or less at Doctor Russell's skillful hands meant little to a boy like Creighton. William, who could not sleep that night, heard Tom moan about welts once or twice between his snores, but that seemed a small penalty for inflicting on a wounded victim a deliberate injury that was to last a lifetime.

If only his mother had not been moving to a new place during his next week-end holiday, William wouldn't have minded his present unhappiness so much. The thought of not being able to go home weighed upon him; he felt that he wanted more than anything to get away from Charterhouse. He knew if he wrote his mother all the details of the fight and the assault by Creighton, she would have him called home at once, but she would be frantic with fear for his health, and make an awful fuss about his nose, and worry herself into a state. So he wrote a letter which merely stated the fact that he had been in a fight, and had been hit in the nose. He would see her and the Major when their next turn came, and he would go somewhere else for this time.

Since his parents couldn't ask him out, William went to the Ritchies'. There was a new baby now, Jane Ritchie. Charlotte was already a little girl, and William a lively lad of five. By good fortune, Richmond was visiting there the same week end. He was sporting a black eye, his right; it was swollen to nearly twice its size, half closed, and violently colored in red, blue, and purple shading into a sickly yellowish green. Beside William's smashed nose, still with a bandage across the broken bridge, it gave the apartment in Southampton Row the air of a hospital for the wounded.

"I see we have a couple of veterans from the public

schools," Uncle John remarked to Aunt Ritchie when he came upstairs for dinner.

She laughed, but her eyes were sympathetic. "Why must these things always happen to boys at school?"

"Because unfortunately fighting is a national schoolboy sport." Their uncle cut into the roast. "What happened, boys?"

"You should just see Clarkson, sir, that's all!" Richmond's clear eye glowed with pride. "*Both* of his are black, and there's a nasty gash on his cheek, and . . . "

But their uncle was laughing. "Yes, yes, the other fellow always gets the worst of it. What about you, Bill?"

William could smile now that it was all over, and Venables was a friend, and Richmond had a black eye. "I guess it was about fifty-fifty, sir," He related what had happened. "Venables had a split lip, but when he hit my nose, it bled so hard they had to stop the fight." He went on to narrate what had taken place a few days later.

When he finished, five-year-old William, who loved a bloody tale, said eagerly, "Tell the story again, Cousin Bill."

But his mother silenced him. "Once is enough, my son. That Creighton boy should be expelled!" She was furious at the unfair assault.

Richmond doubled his fists. "I'd like to have a go at paying him out. We have a few bullies at school, but none of them can compare with this one at Charterhouse!"

"A cowardly deed of the worst sort," was their uncle's verdict.

But Aunt Ritchie was concerned about the state of William's nose. "I'm afraid the second blow may have injured it permanently, so that your breathing will be affected." She touched the swollen places beneath the bandage gently. "I had no idea the bridge was so completely smashed! Can't the bones be patched up someway?"

"At school they decided nothing could be done," William said. He began to feel gloomy again.

"We will take you to see Sir Charles Clarke about it," Aunt Ritchie promised.

"But first we will take you to Astley's," his uncle said. "An evening at Astley's is known to be sure cure for all ills."

"Hurray!" shouted the boys, and little William and Charlotte echoed the cry without knowing why.

After dinner Uncle Ritchie carried the whole family off to the variety hall. Astley's was a sort of indoor circus, with clowns, bareback riders, tumblers and jugglers. It was a favorite entertainment house for family gatherings of young and old, and William had often heard the famous name though he had never been to a performance there.

They sat in one of the boxes that surrounded the arena. All about them were family parties, including grey-haired grandparents and babes in arms. A hawker came by with a basket of oranges, and Uncle Ritchie purchased a supply for everyone. Gay laughter of anticipation, mixed with the chattering of childish voices, came bubbling from the boxes like a joyous song. At Astley's even the oldest felt young again, and the most sober countenance suddenly turned cheerful.

Then the trumpets blared, the bareback riders in gaudy costumes came riding into the ring, and the clowns, with their funny faces, tumbled about like huge, animated toys. How exciting it all was! William leaned forward over the railing of the box in order to get as close as possible. The jugglers performed with miraculous speed, yet they never missed a single catch! The pantomime, showing Napoleon at Waterloo, was spellbinding, thrilling.

"Great, isn't it?" Richmond whispered.

William nodded blissfully without taking his eyes from the arena. When the clowns came out again, he laughed so hard at their antics he nearly choked on his orange, and Aunt

Ritchie had to pat him on the back, and they all laughed harder. In the general jollity he forgot his broken nose, and by the time the show was over, his heart felt as light as the papiermaché plates the jugglers had tossed into the air.

While he and Richmond were undressing for bed, his cousin offered to come to Charterhouse some day for the purpose of punishing the bully. "Between us we ought to be able to beat him," he said fiercely. "The great coward!" His lips, full and red in contrast to his dark, lean face, curled in fine scorn.

"Thanks, Rich." It was good to know he could depend on his cousin's loyalty, but William felt that if he ever got even with Creighton, it must be on his own.

The next morning he drew pictures of the clowns and jugglers for the Ritchie children, who would hardly let him stop. "Make one more, Bill," little Billy kept begging, and two-year-old Charlotte lisped, "More pictcha, more pictcha," until he had filled all the available scraps in the nursery.

In the afternoon his aunt took him to the doctor's, but the verdict was the same: the cartilage was smashed, the bones too badly splintered to repair. "But the damage was done so squarely in the center I don't think it will hamper his breathing much," Sir Charles said. "How does it feel, my boy?"

"As if someone had stuffed a doorknob up there!"

The doctor laughed. "That's the swelling. When it goes down, you won't feel so uncomfortable, but you will have a bridgeless nose."

It was difficult to accept the fact that his face would always be disfigured, but basking in the warmth of the Ritchies' pleasant household, fortified by the good dinners, the bright memory of Astley's and the loyal comradeship of his cousin, he went back to Charterhouse at the end of the two-day period in a much happier frame of mind.

7

School Joys and Sorrows

As soon as his next turn came, William went to Addiscombe, where the Major was head of a military college.

His mother persisted in bemoaning his appearance every time she looked at him during the week end. "Your poor little nose," she said consolingly again and again. And once: "I hoped you would be as handsome as your father, but now it can never be."

His stepfather, on the other hand, adopted a practical attitude toward the affair. He took William out in back of one of the buildings and gave him a few pointers on boxing. "I remember my own days at Charterhouse," he said. "I know how important self-defense in school can be. Perhaps if you had known how to guard with your left, those bones would be in one piece even now. Not that you had a chance against that young scapegrace, Creighton," the Major's kindly face darkened for a moment, "but Venables wouldn't have been able to hit your nose in the first place." He showed William how to hold his left fist before his face while hitting out straight from the shoulder with his right; how to feint; how to develop fast footwork in side-stepping his opponent.

By the time he went back to school, William had learned enough to fortify him against future attacks, and he felt profoundly grateful to his stepfather. Though he hated to say good-bye to his mother, he was slowly growing accustomed to Charterhouse, and could take his return to school as a matter of course.

George Venables and Joe Carne met him at the entrance to

Penny's to regale him with various happenings that had taken place over the week end. Creighton had been called to Dr. Russell's study and put back to the Ninth for cribbing. Moody had got hold of two volumes of "The Mysteries of Udolpho," which he was passing around the dorm at the rate of sixpence to all borrowers.

William was ready to go in search of Moody immediately, but the bells were ringing for class, and they all hurried through the tunnel. He had at last got out of the Tenth form, but the Ninth was still too easy for William, and whenever he could get hold of a novel to read behind the textbooks piled on his desk, he jumped at the chance.

There was no sign of order in the Ninth when he came in. Creighton and some other big boys who, for one reason or another, had been put in the lower form, had started a spitball fight in the back. Two small boys were duelling with their rulers, and the rest were shouting, laughing, whispering after the manner of schoolboys in general. The praepositus who had been set to rule over them, though older than most of them, and in the Fourth form, was a slight, pale boy, much smaller than the band of spitball throwers. In vain he rapped for order. "Gentlemen, come to order. Quiet, please. Quiet!"

But no one felt like settling down. "Quiet, yourself," someone yelled, and another bawled the suggestion, "Put 'im under the desk!"

The words were no sooner out than three of the larger boys seized the poor praepositus and shoved him under the desk in such a way that he couldn't move to get out. Then merriment and chaos reigned supreme. The boys ran around the room, shouted, pushed each other and threw spitballs at a furious rate. William drew an immense caricature of Dr. Russell with exaggerated beak and a bush of shaggy black hair, which he held up for the enjoyment of all.

"I say, look what Thackeray's done — old Russell himself!" The boys shrieked with laughter. "Good for you, Thackeray! Do some more." And William, spurred on by such acclaim, added horns to the head, and a rod in the doctor's hand, upraised to beat a tiny urchin.

When the noise was at its height, the door opened, and the Headmaster himself walked in. William shoved the drawing under his desk quickly, and a few around the door quieted down, but most of the class was in such an uproar they didn't notice the Doctor's entrance until he cried: "Gentlemen, where is your praepositus?"

The boys froze in their positions, and an ominous silence took hold of the room.

"Well," came the question in more threatening tones, "where is your praepositus?"

At first no one would answer. Then a meek boy said, "Please, sir, here he is," pointing to the desk. The deed was out; there was only one thing to do. Several of the boys fished the poor trembling praepositus from under the desk, and stood him before the Headmaster.

Dr. Russell was quivering with rage, which he let out in a mighty roar of invectives hurled at the young "gentlemen," but the boy in front of him was so obviously unfit for the job of teacher that there was little he could do; he threatened and raved, but he knew the fault lay in the system he himself had introduced. He sent the lad back to his own form, saying that he — the Doctor himself — would teach the class that day. (He made a mental note to see that a bigger praepositus was appointed.) "Get out your readers!"

The drawing of Dr. Russell which William had so hastily thrust inside his desk was stuffed in on top of his books, and to take his reader out he had first to remove the crumpled wad. He tried it stealthily, hoping to make no noise, but just as he had succeeded, he dropped the paper on the floor, and as ill luck would have it, the Headmaster happened to be looking in his direction.

"Well, boy, what is the mess you've made there?" he demanded.

"Just some waste paper, sir." William picked it up hastily.

"Bring it here."

"Yes, sir." William rose and handed it to him with trembling fingers, while the class waited breathlessly to see what would happen. The Doctor, being in a black mood, opened the sheet to investigate its contents. When he saw the cartoon, his face became livid. His first impulse was to haul William off to the Block for a thrashing, but the sketch was a bold condemnation of his punishment. The humor of it made him feel uncomfortable, so he turned to the only weapon he knew how to use in return, heavy-handed sarcasm.

"Boy, what is your name?"

"Thackeray, sir."

"I believe you have been misnamed. I think you should be called Rembrandt!"

A snicker went over the class, which was exactly the effect he desired. "Thackeray, eh?" he went on. "Now I remember: I knew you were an idle pupil from our first interview. This proves it." In renewed rage he tore the drawing to bits and threw them in the wastebasket. Then, picking up two books, he put William's head between them and boxed his ears sharply. "Now return to your seat," he commanded, "and let us have no more demonstrations of genius." He delivered a few more slights and insults against William's talent, and proceeded to the reading lesson.

In spite of the Doctor's belittling attitude, the caricature brought William his first taste of school fame. The incident was repeated in the lower and upper forms, and the boys soon began to make appeals that Thackeray should draw this scene or that. He was happy to have discovered a means of winning more friends and a certain degree of respect among his fellow-students. His textbooks became full of sketches of Melmoth the Wanderer, from the novel of the day, of the heroes and villains in the mysteries that made their way around the dorm.

He found others besides himself who were interested in these tales — Carne, Venables, Liddell, and some slightly older boys, Martin Tupper and John Murray. How fascinating the novels were! He spent whole afternoons drinking them in. He escaped from the games by the simple method of discrediting himself before the other players had a chance.

"Here comes the worst player on the team," he would admit cheerfully when he came up to bat in cricket. And when, as usual, he struck out, he would exclaim, "Good old Thackeray! What did I tell you? You can always depend on him to lose the game for you!" So instead of games he could take recreation in reading, and he filled himself to the fullest.

"I like novels without love or talking or any of that nonsense," he confided to Carne. "Just give me plenty of fighting, escaping, robbing and rescuing." His eyes glowed and he found himself unconsciously sketching the peaked cap of Thaddeus of Warsaw, the hero of whom he had just been reading.

"Go on," Carne said. "Finish it."

So William outlined the face: first the eyes, bold and flashing; then the nose, straight and strong — "no hero could have a nose like mine," he joked — and finally the full curving lips, surmounted by long, curling mustachios.

"I wish I could draw." Carne's bright eyes were following the strokes intently.

"It's easy — just watch." And William continued with the rounded lines of muscular shoulders. A flashy uniform with embroidered tights and dangling sword came next, and last of all he sketched in the tasselled Hessian boots the heroes wore. He moistened his pencil and filled them in to a shiny black. "If only I had a pair like that!" he sighed as he completed them. He dug down into his trunk and pulled out a clothing catalog he had picked up at the Ritchies'. Turning to the shoe section, he pointed to the illustration showing a pair of boots exactly like those he had drawn. "Look, there they are!"

"Beauties, all right," murmured Carne.

"Wouldn't I love to wear those on the Green, that's all!" William said. He wished he had not spent his money so freely on tarts for himself and his friends. "Even my stepfather forgot to tip me when I was home."

"How would you get the boots if you did have the money?" asked Carne.

"I'd order them," William said grandly. And after a moment, "I'll do it, too! I'll save all my tips till I have enough."

Just then George Venables came up, full of excitement. "I say, Bill, Joe — Fawsett minor's got a hamper from home!"

"Hurray for Walter!" The boys put away the catalog and hurried after George, footwear temporarily forgotten.

"Of course the basket's for Fawsett major, too," George reminded them. "He and Walter were just reading their mother's letter when I came to fetch you."

When the trio reached the lower hall, the brothers were reading the last lines, while a number of their classmates knelt by the basket, trying to get a glimpse of its contents, peeking under the lid where it wasn't tied down. At last the letter was folded and put away and Fawsett major took the knife Mr. Penny had offered and cut the ropes.

"You're just in time!" Walter called out as the three came up. His face was flushed and happy and he was well aware that for the moment the Fawsetts were the center of attraction at Penny's. Even the master, who stood part with Mr. Churton, the Upper Form master, watched the proceedings with a benevolent eye. At Charterhouse a hamper from

home represented a stroke of good fortune, and the masters, besides enjoying the event, stood by to see that Creighton or some other bully didn't take advantage of Walter when he received his share. Besides the bullies, the school had a few pirates who had been known to make off with the sweets of small boys before they realized what was taking place.

This wonderful storehouse of treasures from home contained a game pie for each of the boys, two bottles of currant wine, several jampots, a cake, and a quantity of pears packed in the straw. In addition, there were two coin purses netted by Mrs. Fawsett, one for Walter, in which gleamed five shiny shillings, and one for his brother with the more dignified sum of a sovereign.

The unpacking was accompanied by exclamations of, "Oh, game pie!" and "Ah, cake!" and many other interested remarks from the onlookers. Enemies of the Fawsetts suddenly became mellow and friendly. Tom Creighton hung around hoping for a favor, but Walter ignored him.

That night there was a feast in the dorm for all of Walter's cronies: Venables, Carne, Moody and Thackeray. And Creighton made himself so pleasant, the young host wavered and gave him some of the game pie and currant wine along with the rest. It was after-hours, and they should have been asleep, and food from home was supposed to be kept in the cook's pantry, all of which added to the delightful flavor of the fare. The meat pie was followed by a slice of cake and pears and more wine. Carne sang a song, and offered to tell his most dreadful story, "if you'll give me another slice of cake, Fawsett."

"Agreed!" cried Walter, picking up the penknife, and cutting a generous piece. His sense of importance exhilarated him. "How about you, Thackeray? Will you draw us a picture of Dr. Russell for another slice?"

"As many as you like!" William held out his plate. This was the experience he had been waiting for, and the warm friendly glow deep inside him was not entirely caused by the currant wine. At last he was part of the school: part of the whispered jokes, the laughter, the secret doings of boys, among which a "midnight feast" held first place.

As they were all snickering over Carne's story, Venables suddenly held up a warning finger. "Shh! The masters!" The others had not heard the sound, but they stopped to listen now. Sure enough, there was an audible clearing of throats in the corridor, and then a short but distinct conversation between Penny and Churton.

"Hurry, help me!" Fawsett quickly pushed the cake under the bed, along with the remains of the game pie, while the others shoved the bottle of wine, the glasses and the pears in after them. They blew out the candle in their midst, and dived into bed. When Mr. Penny opened the door, all was dark and still; one or two quite realistic snores might even be heard. And if the master smelled the paraffin of the snuffed candle, he seemed to take no notice of it, but closed the door softly again as he reported to Churton, "All quiet."

The boys went to sleep with full stomachs and fuller hearts. True, some of them might be obliged to accept the services of the school doctor in the morning, but the party had been a complete success: they had had their fun without being discovered.

But if the red-nosed master of the lower form had his rare moments of generosity toward the pupils, he did not allow them to know it. William, especially, was convinced that Reverend Penny had no true feeling for the things a schoolboy holds most dear. On the Sunday after Fawsett's feast, the Carmichael-Smyths came to visit their son. When they left, William's mother gave him a five-shilling piece, and his stepfather, who tipped his friends as well, came forth with the usual sovereign for Bill. (The boys were charmed with his mother, and "Thackeray's governor" was considered first-rate because of his tipping all around.)

William vowed to his mother that he would not spend the five shillings until he had been promoted to the Eighth form — he intended asking for the promotion the next day. He did not say what he was going to do with the sovereign, but he had a plan.

"Know how I'm going to spend the tip from my governor?" he asked Carne when they were alone.

"On tarts, three-cornered puffs and brandy balls." Joe knew his favorite pastries.

"Wrong! I shall order those Hessian boots — tomorrow. What a stroke of luck. I never thought to have the money so soon."

"Are you really going to buy them?" Joe was incredulous.

"I'll write the order now." William fished out the catalog, found the address, scribbled the lines and enclosed his sovereign with them in an envelope while Joe admiringly watched his determined movements.

Of course Venables had to be told of the purchase, and the news soon spread through Penny's house that Thackeray was getting a pair of Hessian boots. During the two weeks before their arrival, he had described them so often and with such imagination that the mere thought of his appearing in them created a sensation, and the boys were already bargaining for the loan of his famous boots — at a price, of course.

At last the package was delivered. With a ring of spectators surrounding him, William opened it, his fingers clumsy in their eagerness. He removed the boots from the layer of wrappings — they were black, shined to a high gloss, pointed, tasseled, altogether as dashing as he had predicted. No hamper from home was ever greeted with more enthusiastic cries of admiration.

"Try them on, Bill!" Venables urged.

"Yes, yes, we want to see how they look."

William took off his bluchers, and pulled on the magnificent boots. How they shone, glistening like polished black marble! How rakish the tassels were! He swaggered across the room, feeling like Thaddeus of Warsaw himself — he needed only the sword and Polish cap. He strutted back toward the other side again, the envious glances of his schoolmates like wine in his brain. To think he possessed something they longed for! His future prestige was assured.

At this supreme moment, Mr. Penny came in. He eyed the boots critically, his thick, coarse lips pursed. "Thackeray, where did you get those monstrosities?" he demanded finally.

"I ordered them from Henley's, sir."

"You will send them back at once."

"But Mr. Penny . . ." William's heart crumpled within him.

"They are unfit for a schoolboy to wear; we will have no arguments about the matter. I know Dr. Russell will uphold my decision."

It was a harsh edict — after all his bragging, to have to send back the parcel! He couldn't give up without a struggle. "Please, Mr. Penny, mayn't I wear them once on the Green?" he pleaded.

"You may not, sir." Mr. Penny was unmoved. "Unless you want to feel the sting of Dr. Russell's birch rod, you will do as I say immediately."

"Yes, sir." William sat down and slowly pulled off the beloved Hessian boots. The thought of Dr. Russell's wrath had forced him to submit. But it was so humiliating. He couldn't look at his schoolmates. His blaze of glory had been snuffed out just as it was kindling. No amount of sweets or treasures which his returned sovereign would buy could make up for such a loss.

"I shall never forget what Penny is making me do as long as I live," he swore to himself as he wrapped up the boots once more. His eyes were bleak and very bitter.

8

Larkbeare

A YEAR AND A HALF LATER, William was at his favorite pastime, marking off the days of December, 1825, on the calendar. He had advanced to the Fifth form, and he was to spend December holidays at his first real home since Alipur. For the Major and his mother had leased a small country estate, called Larkbeare, near Ottery St. Mary in Devon. It gave him a singular thrill to think he would have a place he could mention carelessly like the rest of the boys. What was it again? he consulted the letter. "Larkbeare, Larkbeare." He repeated the name several times. It had a good sound. Now he could say to Carne or Venables, "Will you come down to Larkbeare next Eastertide?" as he had so often heard the others invite their friends to their homes.

When Christmastime came, and he was actually bound for Exeter, the town nearest Larkbeare, he could hardly believe his good fortune. The weather was bitingly cold. When he changed coaches at Exeter the inside places were all taken, and he was bundled up on the top. A student from Cambridge loaned him a blanket, but still his teeth chattered. There was snow on the ground, and the driver took his time over the winding, hilly roads, dangerous for fast-travelling horses. William dozed after awhile, benumbed with cold, and the next thing he knew the coach

Coachee.

67

came to a sudden stop at a byroad branching off the main highway. In the dimness he could see a carriage waiting, and when the coachman called "Tallaton Road!" he knew it must have come from Larkbeare to meet him.

He tried to stand up, but he was too stiff — he felt frozen. "I can't move," he said hoarsely to the Cambridge student, fearful that the mail would start up again if he didn't get off.

"Here, I'll help you." The young man lifted him up. "Halloo, down there! Boy coming down half-frozen."

At his words a sturdy little man in mustard-colored plush breeches and enormous greatcoat, who had been conferring with the driver, came up on a run. "I say, Master Thackeray, is it you, sir?"

"Yes."

"We'll get you down, sir." The man had climbed up in a moment, lifted William over the side and into the carriage, talking all the while. "A bloomin' shame they shoved you hup top, develish cold night like this! I'm John Golds-worthy, you know, lad, what worked for your mother's family years back, an' now me an' Martha — my wife — have come to Larkbeare to work for the Mijer and your mother, bless 'er, she's that kind!" He piled blankets around William as he rambled on.

The boy was too drowsy and cold to take notice of all the details of John's past and present history, but he felt a new security in being so well cared for by the friendly, efficient, garrulous servant.

After they had passed the sleeping village, they went down an overhanging beech avenue which skirted a lonely, tree-fringed pond that William could just make out beyond the road. He wondered if there would be good fishing here. They reached the gates of Larkbeare at last, turned

into the sweep, and in a moment drew up before the wel-
coming portals of the square-faced house. Larkbeare was by
no means a mansion, but one look at its pleasant center hall
in which a fire was burning, its low, beamed ceilings and
long, casement windows told William this would be home,
not just some place you went to meet your parents when the
holidays came.

His mother, on the other hand, who was waiting for him
in the hall, needed only one look at William to tell her
there was cause for alarm. "Oh, Billy boy, you're half
frozen!" Always easily upset about his welfare, she pulled
him over to the fireplace and began to undo the fastenings
of his coat. "Tell Martha to bring a tumbler of hot blackberry cordial," she instructed John. "I do hope you won't
come down with pneumonia, my son."

"Don't worry, Mamma, I can thaw out as well as any icicle
— especially with the help of blackberry cordial," he added
impishly as Martha Goldsworthy, a motherly housekeeper
with a snowy white neckerchief and cap, brought in the
steaming tumbler.

"Of course he'll thaw out, and be right as rain in the
morning," was the Major's opinion as he came from the
library to greet his stepson. "I remember many a time I
nearly froze to death coming home for the holidays. Welcome to Larkbeare, Bill!" He shook William's hand and
asked, eagerly, "How do you like it?"

"First-rate, sir, from what I've seen. Reminds me of
Alipur."

"Oh." The Major did not seem too well pleased.

"I mean . . . it's like home, you see, Pa." Sometimes he
called the major Pa in his letters, just for fun; sometimes he
called him "governor," as the other boys did their fathers.
"I haven't come *home* since I've been at school."

"I see." The Major smiled happily, his good nature restored. He was anxious to have William look upon him as a father. Though he had been kind to the boy since he and William's mother had returned from India, there had been no true feeling of family among the three of them, and the Major hoped Larkbeare would bring it about.

When he had been warmed through by the fire and cordial, William's mother showed him to his room, where flames also glowed on the hearth, and the polished oaken bed, desk, wardrobe and cosy little window bench reflected a warm welcome. His room — his very own. He had wanted one for so long!

"It's mine, isn't it? For always?" His voice caught the least bit.

His mother took his hand, smiling. "As long as we are at Larkbeare. Do you like it?"

"Couldn't be any better!" He jounced the bed a few times and sat on it. "And can I ask Carne to visit? And Venables?"

"Venables? Isn't he the one who smashed your nose?"

"Not really. They patched it up you know, the first time." His mother seemed to have only a vague idea of what had happened, but he didn't want to talk about it. "Anyhow, Venables and I became cronies after that, the way everyone does. There's nothing like a good fight to help you make friends!"

But Mrs. Carmichael-Smyth didn't see the joke. She was a woman of great sweetness and purity, and very little humor. "I should prefer you to make friends through charity and acts of kindness rather than violence."

"Don't worry, mother." He put his arms around her. "I'm not boxing my way up the school, at least." Seeing her puzzled expression, he explained, "It's like this: if I'd licked

A Happy Family, Probably Thackeray's Version
of the Ritchies

View From Aunt Ritchie's House on Southampton Row

Shiner

Old John

A Stern Master

After School

Thackeray's Sketches From His School Days

Venables, who can thrash Bedford, how much more could I have licked Bedford, and so on up. Don't you see?"

But his mother did not see. Such talk distressed her, so she said, "I think you had better go to bed now, my dear. Are you sure you're not cold any longer?"

He convinced her that he was quite warm, and after kissing him good-night, with an admonition not to forget his prayers, his mother left him. Once alone, he began a complete inspection tour of the room. He tried the drawers in the wardrobe, and made faces at his image in the mirror above it. He sat at the desk and drew a little sketch of his domain, including the canopied bed and high latticed windows hung with green stuff drapes. He stretched out on the padded window bench, put his hands behind his neck and crossed his legs in leisurely fashion. His eyes roamed around, planning improvements. He would make some drawings to hang on the walls. He would beg his mother for a bookcase to place beside the desk, and fill it with his favorite novels — pack it full of mysteries and then he could lie here on the bench and read and read . . . and read . . .

The bedside candle sputtered in its cup, flickered, and went out. The fire burned down to embers in the grate, and its dull red deepened the curve of the smile on his peaceful, sleeping face.

The next day he spent going over the grounds of Larkbeare. In the daylight, he saw that the house had a white portico and seven straight windows across the front. The lawns were bumpy and uneven, and there was a little green door in the wall of the yard which led into them. The yard, its hard mud surface strewn with straw, had stables large enough to house Prince and Blucher, the carriage horses, and perhaps there would be room for a little mare next summer, the Major hinted. "Dr. Cornish, the Vicar, says one of the Ottery tenants will offer a filly for sale in the spring. Would you like to be her master, Bill?"

"You mean I'd have a pony, like Lord Beaumont's son at school?"

The Major laughed. "I doubt if she'll measure up to the baronet's steed, my son, but since Dr. Cornish has recommended the farmer, I daresay she'll carry you around the countryside all right."

It was too good to be true. William had secretly longed to possess a pony, which was considered the mark of a gentleman at Charterhouse. Although he had slowly earned friends and something of a reputation for good humor and talent, he continued to feel the need of establishing himself on a solid basis. Schoolboys are quick to sense insecurity, and when Thackeray kept going off to different towns to meet his parents, they set him down privately as a waif. He had a stepfather, to begin with, and no real home — nothing that belonged to him. This attitude was never openly expressed, but William felt it nevertheless, and probably exaggerated it somewhat.

After the boys had met the Major and Mrs. Carmichael-Smyth, they were more generous in their opinion of William's background, and with the purchase of Larkbeare, not to mention a pony of his own, he hoped to be considered a true gentleman's son, as he knew himself to be.

During the afternoon he explored the woods, and found a rotten old boat tied to a rickety dock on the pond. The water was frozen and caked around the ancient craft, but he stepped into it and tried out the seats and examined the floor. A little caulking would fix it up. If Carne came down in the spring, they could use it for fishing. He would get John Goldsworthy to strengthen the dock, so they could lie on it and catch minnows.

He walked to the village, passing along the way Ottery Hall, the manor house from which Ottery St. Mary took its name. The mansion was deserted, its huge, oaken portals flaked and peeled, its knocker dirty and rusted. The terrace was overrun, the west wall crumbling. Only a few rooms in one wing were inhabited, and these by a couple of servants who were left on the estate to look out for poachers. Many years later William was to describe the hall in detail, for it was to be the scene of action in a considerable part of his novel, "Pendennis." But as he ambled by it now, he thought of how ghostly it looked, like a second "Castle of Otranto," the mystery he had been reading. Just the place for a game of "outlaw."

Over the top of the slope which led from Ottery Hall, the village came into view, like a little calendar picture of a quiet country hamlet, nestling among the rounded hills with its single church steeple rising into the sky, and a glimpse of the sea in the distance. "When I come again, I'll bring a pencil and sketching pad," William thought.

He went down into the main street, past the empty marketplace and the small shops to the inn, where he watched the coaches come in, discharging weary passengers, changing wearier horses. On the way back, he stepped into the church for a moment. The pale winter sunlight only half lit up its dim interior. He tiptoed down the aisle toward the chancel, feeling that he ought not to disturb the peaceful silence. Suddenly there was a clatter of tools on the floor, and the white, woolly head of a portly gentleman of the clergy appeared over the top of the railing.

"Odd's life!" he panted. "A fine state of affairs when the Vicar himself must repair his own chancel. Give me a hand here, will you, my son?"

"Yes, sir, I'll be glad to help you." Surprised, and somewhat amused at the sight of the dignified minister rising up like a troll with his face red and perspiring, William ran to assist him. One of the crossbars had loosened, and he was trying to hammer it back into place.

"The curate had to go into Exeter, the sexton is sick abed, and only the good Lord knows — though I suspect — where Jerry, the carpenter, is at a time like this," grumbled the man. "Just hold the bar in place, my boy."

"Yes, sir." William grasped it firmly. "Hammer away, sir."

In a few minutes the job was done. "Ah, that's better." The man straightened up, pressing his palms into the small of his back. "What's your name, lad? I don't remember seeing you in church."

"I just came to Larkbeare last night, so you couldn't have seen me, but I expect you know my mother already, sir — Mrs. Carmichael-Smyth."

"Yes, of course, and the Major — the new owners of Larkbeare. You're their son."

"The Major is my stepfather, sir. I'm William Makepeace Thackeray."

"'Makepeace.'" The Vicar looked him over thoughtfully. "Think you can live up to it?"

William smiled. "I hope so, sir. It belonged to one of my ancestors, a stout yeoman who served as peacemaker, so my relations say. Are you Dr. Cornish?"

"The same, and I'm glad to make your acquaintance, my boy." He took William's arm. "Come, we'll introduce you to Mrs. Cornish."

They went to the Rectory next door, where the Vicar's wife, as portly as her husband, and twice as voluble, made William feel at home with a cup of tea and a recital of village doings. The Vicar, discovering that his new young neighbor liked to read, offered any books in his library that William would care to try.

It was twilight when he reached home, and during the quiet evening after dinner, William recounted his day's activities to his family. The Major was stretched out comfortably, a short military cape or poncho around his shoulders, and his mother worked a delicate piece of petit point as she listened. Both of them were pleased to find William so well satisfied with his new surroundings.

The days passed all too quickly. The Christmas mince pies had never tasted so good as they did this year. The lights of the tree had never shone so brightly. He hated to think of going back to school. "If only it would be more like home," he said to his mother on one of the last nights. "Penny's house is so crowded and noisy that you hardly have a chance to think. And Mr. Penny is so coarse and mean." He drew her a sketch of the fat lips and bulbous nose, the thick, pudgy fingers shaking threateningly at some pupil.

"You ought not to make fun of your masters, William," his mother reproved him. But she laughed at the drawing, and thought to herself that she had a clever son. "I have been considering the idea of placing you in a boardinghouse near the school. Would you like to be a day-boy?"

"A day-boy! Yes, oh yes, it would be so much better!" William put his arms around his mother. "When can I start? Right away?"

"I will have to come to London and find a suitable place. But perhaps by next term it can be arranged," his mother said.

And with this bright promise he took the coach from Exeter a day or so later, knowing that he would count the weeks until he returned to Larkbeare the next time.

9

Retribution

IN SPITE of the fact that he was quite convinced he hated Charterhouse, William found himself enjoying the reunion with his classmates after the holidays. The long-room at Penny's was full when Carne, Venables and he, having exchanged experiences privately in the dormitory, sauntered downstairs to see what the rest of their fellows were about.

Above the general din they could hear a commotion of some sort going on toward the front of the room where Creighton and a group of his consorts surrounded a small table.

"Creighton seems up to his usual tricks," William remarked. "Wonder what the master mind is scheming about this time."

Carne laughed but George Venables asserted, "Whatever it is he's up to no good."

Just then a seven-year-old boy was lifted off the floor bodily and set upon the table, his face flushed, his blue sailor suit crumpled and awry.

"You're right, George. Come on." William pushed forward and the other two followed him. Somehow he felt he must protect the little fellow if he possibly could.

"Go ahead, let's hear you," Creighton was commanding as the three came up. "You said you could sing — well, give us a little entertainment." He let out a loud guffaw in which the rest joined.

The newcomer's face grew red, and William, watching him, remembered his own initiation to Charterhouse at Creighton's hands. How unhappy the bully had made him

that first night! He and Creighton were still at swords'
point, though there were brief periods of truce between
them. Seeing this boy's discomfiture, he was ready to step
up and take his part, when the little fellow suddenly opened
his mouth and began to sing "Home, Sweet Home" in a
strong, lusty voice. He continued unfalteringly through to
the end, his plucky spirit commanding the respectful silence
of his listeners.

"Bravo!" cried William when the song was ended. He
went up and clapped the small, blue-clad shoulder. "Well-
sung, Carthusian!" He called the boy by the name given to
anyone attending Charterhouse.

"Thank you." The round face lit up, happy to find a
friend.

"What's your name, boy?" William began the routine
questions.

"John Leech." — "How old are you?" — "Seven and a
half."

"Who's your father?"

There was a silence. Then: "My father's dead. My
mother has taken rooms across the Square, so she can see me
when we come out on the Green."

A derisive roar came from Creighton. "Mamma's going
to keep an eye on her little angel, is she?"

William's fists doubled up, but he pretended not to notice
the rude jeer. "That's fine, Leech! Come, I'll help you
down." He decided not to ask how much money the boy
had. It might prove embarrassing or give Creighton a
chance for further torture.

"Just a minute, Thackeray." The bully of Penny's house
barred the way. "I didn't say he could get down."

"No, you said enough as it is." William met the other's
eye and stared him into silence.

No one had laughed at Tom Creighton's taunt, and he felt a sense of shame, not only for his jibe, but for the way the chubby youngster had stood up and sung. Moreover — and this was perhaps the most important reason for his retreat — he noticed with alarm that William's shoulders nearly measured his in breadth, and their eyes were almost on a level. His chief target was getting too big — he had best lay low. "What do I care?" he shrugged. "Do as you please. I've got a bottle of currant wine. Who wants a drink?" And he paraded off, a few of his faithful marching somewhat dubiously in his wake.

Little John Leech and William soon became good friends despite the difference in their ages. Once a week all the boys at Penny's had drawing lessons in the Gownboy writing room from the drawing-master, Mr. Burgess. His old-fashioned methods did not include comic sketching but William persisted in it despite the master's instruction. The new pupil appeared to possess the same kind of talent, and William was delighted to find someone who shared his ability for caricature.

The younger boy's work was still quite undeveloped, but he showed great possibilities. He drew Tom Creighton's portrait, a gawky figure with flapping ears and huge paws for hands and feet, when he was supposed to be copying designs out of an ancient art manual. He nudged William and showed off the picture under the desk, and the two enjoyed the ridicule with stifled squeals behind their hands. After that, they had many private sessions together when William showed John how to draw more sharply and how to point up the humor of a situation. Although he was nearly twice as tall as the newcomer, the pair were often seen together.

Tom Creighton was quick to notice the attachment and

to make the most of it. Meeting William on the Green late one afternoon when the playground was deserted, he called out derisively, "Where's your shadow, Thackeray? Can't you get him to follow you around any longer?"

It was a raw January day, and William had been shivering as he returned to Penny's from having delivered a message to one of the Codds but he suddenly felt a surge of heat at Tom's words, and just as suddenly he felt strong, as strong as Creighton, and just as secure. Didn't he have a home, and a pony promised for next spring? His muscles itched for action, and his fists doubled unconsciously.

Without warning, he swung with his right (remembering to protect his nose with his left) and landed a blow squarely on Tom's chin. The enemy went down, completely taken by surprise. He lay on the ground, rubbing his jaw in bewilderment. "What's the idea, Thackeray?" he demanded when he could speak.

"Only that I'm fed up with your bullying and your insults." William glowered down at him menacingly. "Also, we have a score to settle, and now is as good a time as any. Get up!"

"If that's the way you're going to talk!" The unseated champion rose, his eyes red with anger. He shot out a fist, but William was too quick for it and dodged successfully.

Then they both pitched into each other with fury, but William was able to parry blow for blow and get in a few extra on his own. Creighton fought blindly, seething with anger. At last William planted his fist so squarely that Tom went down and could not get up. Just as he fell, Venables, Carne and John Leech, who had come out to meet William and saw the struggle, rushed to the scene with cries of, "Bill, what's the trouble?"

"I licked him," William gasped, hardly able to believe it

himself. With the back of his hand he brushed the blood from a gash on his cheek. "I licked Creighton!" He had paid the bully out at last.

Within half an hour the word had swept through Penny's, on to Churton's house, and through the rest of the school: "Thackeray licked Creighton!" It spread like wildfire. It was the news of the hour. A tyrant had been unseated, a despot dethroned. Such an event was not infrequent in the history of Charterhouse; there was a change of dictators every once in awhile.

But for Bill Thackeray to assail and lick Tom Creighton — it was like a breeze battling a tornado, a mourning dove tearing into a fighting cock. William had a reputation for mildness and humorous indolence; that he must have become cyclonic as well for a few moments was the wonder of the day. How had it come about?

No one could say, not even the hero. Indeed, no one was more incredulous of the whole event than William himself. It had all happened so quickly, in much less time than it took to tell the story afterward. "It's hard to explain," he insisted to Venables, Carne, Fawsett and a few others gathered to hear a detailed account from the lips of the victor. He was sprawled on his bed, resting, his face decorated with a piece of court plaster across the gash. "I don't know what took hold of me, but all of a sudden I felt a white flash of anger go down my back; I was so mad I could see it. At the same time, every cowardly act of Creighton's rose up in front of me, and I clenched my hands so hard my nails went into my skin." He displayed the marks they had left on his palms, his own eyes unbelieving. He shook his head, wondering still how he had ever screwed up his courage and strength.

"Then what?" Joe Carne was growing impatient.

"Well, then I must have put in my right good and solid, because the next thing I knew, there was Goliath on the ground." William couldn't help crowing a little. "Wasn't he surprised, though! I wish all of you had been there."

The others sighed. Every one of them would have given a good deal to have witnessed the sight of Creighton receiving his due. Joe and George described in detail the final tableau of the battle, and John chimed in eagerly. The three assumed a position second in importance only to William.

IO

Polly Graham Comes to Larkbeare

SOME WEEKS after the fight, Major and Mrs. Carmichael-Smyth travelled up to Charterhouse to arrange the matter of lodgings for William in a good boardinghouse, and to confer with the doctor about accepting him as a day-boy. The home of Mr. and Mrs. Benjamin Boyes at 7 Charterhouse Square had been recommended to them, and it did not take long for William to decide that he liked the large room which looked out on the Square, and which he would share with one other boy, a pupil at the Merchant Taylor's school. Mrs. Boyes seemed to be a woman who understood boys. She had a son, Freddy, about William's age, and she had boarded day-pupils for several years. "We make our young men feel right at home," she said. "I don't believe in being stern with children."

Nothing could have suited Mrs. Carmichael-Smyth more. When the question of rates had been settled, and the next term fixed as the time William would enter, they went to Dr. Russell's office to make the necessary arrangements with the Headmaster.

At Eastertide Joe Carne accompanied William to Larkbeare, in the long-hoped-for holiday visit. The two set out on a fresh April morning, riding on the top of the coach where they could look out with the zest of thirteen-year-old boys at a world which seemed as shining to them as the morning sky. Maids in white caps were washing down the front steps of the lovely houses of Mayfair, footmen in livery might be seen opening the blinds of the lower floor windows to let the day come in, and in the stables, grooms were currying the horses against the demands of riders and drivers later on. Rotten Row was deserted at this hour, only an occasional rider, or a barouche decorated with coat of arms and laden with sleepy-eyed revellers returning from a ball, broke into the stillness of the fashionable promenade. In Cheapside, the hawkers were beginning to set up their carts, the merchants prepared their stalls, and top-hatted bankers took their way past St. Paul's to the Bank of England or the Royal Exchange. The city of London was waking up.

Joe's bright eyes snapped with delight. "This is some better than being plagued with old Penny and his Latin declensions, ain't it, Bill?"

William nodded, not taking his eyes off the sights of Town. "Or listening to the doctor's stupid sermons on death and salvation. We'd be in Chapel this minute at Charterhouse," he reminded Joe. At the thought of school the air outside seemed freer than ever, and he breathed in deeply. What a wonderful morning!

The hackney took them to the Bolt-in-Tun, Fleet Street, where they were to catch the mail coach. The boys scrambled over the side, marched into the coffeeroom, and ordered a huge breakfast with a fine, careless manner, like seasoned travelers. They ate at every stop along the way, and made conversation with passengers on the mail, and threw a penny or two to the urchins who swarmed around as the coach came riding up to the various inns.

At Exeter William began to point out familiar landmarks, and at the Tallaton Road they found John Goldsworthy standing by with the family carriage.

"We've two surprises waiting for you at Larkbeare, Master William," the servant said as he helped them in.

"John, you rascal, tell us what they are now," William commanded in a lordly tone. "I don't want to wait till we're home."

But it did him no good. John was not to be impressed by the fact that William had brought along a crony from school. The man's frosty eyes twinkled as he took the reins and said, " 'Twouldn't be no surprise then, and the Major said I wasn't to tell."

William was fairly certain that the promised pony was partly the cause of this mysterious manner, but he couldn't imagine what the other "surprise" was to be. He could tell from the set of John's shoulders, however, that he would get no more out of Mr. Goldsworthy. That trusty man-of-all-work, with his oversize clothes, which always included yellow plush breeches, had an immovable will when it came to doing what he thought was right. He was to serve William faithfully to the end of his days, not only as a valet in later years, but as the model for the manservant in "Pendennis," and that gossipy butler, Jeames Yellowplush, whom William invented for the pleasure of London readers.

Spring had come to Ottery St. Mary early, and on the rough lawns at Larkbeare the beds of stock and wallflowers were already budded. The fruit trees foamed white with bloom against the south wall of the kitchen garden, where later on big yellow egg-plums would crowd, and cherries tempt the robins. Seen in the spring, Larkbeare was more delightful than ever, and William displayed it with pride.

"Of course it isn't a great house, like Beans Beaumont's, but we'll find plenty to do. Wait till you see the improvements I made in my room since I sketched it for you," he finished as the carriage drove into the sweep and drew up before the door.

His mother and the Major were standing on the front

stoop, and with them, almost hidden behind Mrs. Carmichael's grey taffeta skirts, was a small girl of nine or ten. She hung back while William greeted his parents affectionately and Joe presented his respects. She came forward shyly only when Mrs. Carmichael-Smyth put an arm around her. "Don't hide away, Mary dear. William, do you know who this is?"

Whenever his mother called him William, she usually expected him to live up to her expectations. What he saw was a pale child with her hair in braids, neatly attired in a white dress with a blue sash. Her enormous brown eyes stared solemnly back at him as he looked her over. He wasn't sure he remembered her at all, but he thought of something his mother had written in her letters a few months back. " 'Mary' . . . It's Polly; Polly Graham!"

"Yes, yes!" The girl smiled and her eyes lost some of their bigness, their forlornness. "You did know me. Aunt Anne said you would, but I thought you couldn't. . . ."

"Polly is to be my ward," Mrs. Carmichael-Smyth said. "She is going to live with us, so Larkbeare won't be so lonely while you're at school."

William knew why she was to be there. Her mother and father had been cut down by the same deadly fever that destroyed his father. Within a few days one had followed the other, leaving Mary an orphan with only a meager inheritance to provide for her. William's mother, as Mrs. Graham's closest relative, was chosen the logical guardian for the child, and he knew she would be well taken care of under the tender eye of his mother. But at the moment Mary must be feeling more lost than he when he had first come to England. How terrible if his mother had been taken from him along with his father!

He wanted to say a few words to show his sympathy, but what were they to be? It would be ridiculous to offer, "I'm sorry"; everybody knew that. So he teased her a little: "When I come home for vacations, you'll be here to bother me, like Carne's sisters."

"Like those silly, meddlesome creatures? Never!" Joe put in, and the edge of a smile appeared on Polly's lips.

His mother said, "William, what do you mean? Mary won't annoy you in any way."

But the little girl was as pleased as if he had paid her a high compliment. "Shall I really be your sister?" she begged.

"Of course," William told her grandly. "And I shall chaff you and abuse you, and Carne or Venables will write verses to you when you begin to grow up."

Polly laughed outright at last, while Mrs. Carmichael-Smyth shook her head fondly at her son.

The Major pressed William's arm, at the same time taking hold of Carne's. "I have waited long enough. Come, gentlemen; we have business in the yard."

The three started toward the stableyard. Mrs. Carmichael-Smyth, with a mild, "And we have lessons to learn," herded Mary into the house. But a few seconds later William looked back and saw her following them at a safe distance, tagging along toward the stalls, like any younger sister.

The Major hurried along the stable walk to the last stall. "Here we are! I hope you haven't forgotten the filly, my boy. Bring her out, John." He opened the gate wide, and John, who had come back to see that all was in readiness as soon as he deposited the boys, led the yearling into the yard.

She was a slim, sleek-flanked filly, dark brown, nearly black. Her coat shone like the Major's medals, and her eyes were friendly. She was a perfect little mount, and William might ride her around the countryside whenever he chose. His pony. He stepped close to her without a word, and stroked the narrow, satiny bridge of her nose. "I guess *you*

Card Sharpers
A Heartfelt Portrait by Thackeray

As Thackeray Pictured His Life as a Law Student

Books, Books, Books!   *Nightmares*

haven't a broken nose," he whispered, and she nuzzled him thoughtfully.

"Well, will she do?" the Major wanted to know.

"She's exactly what I was hoping for, sir. I say, Carne, take a look!" He made way for Joe beside him, and they went over the pony carefully — mouth, withers, flanks, hooves, all — while little Polly stood on one foot and timidly put out a hand now and then to stroke the animal's side. She was not a rider, having known little of horses in India.

The Major slipped away with a nod to John Goldsworthy as the three youngsters stood hovering over the pony. He had seen enough to tell him that William was more than satisfied, and he wanted no speeches of gratitude.

There was, though, the matter of a name to be settled before they could think of trying the pony out.

"How about Atalanta?" Joe suggested, referring to the fleet-footed heroine of mythology. "She's bound to be fast, then."

"Reminds me too much of Dr. Russell's beloved Greek exercises." William turned up his nose in distaste. "She has such faithful eyes. Let's call her Rachel. What do you say?"

"If you like — she's your pony." Joe looked as though he could have chosen a more exciting name, but William seemed pleased he had found one so fitting. The pony gave promise of being loyal and patient, like Jacob's wife.

He went to the kitchen and begged a few lumps of sugar from Martha, and as he held them out to the filly, he repeated the name several times: "Here, Rachel . . . Another lump for Rachel . . . Come on, Rachel . . ." stepping a short distance away, "Come to me if you want another."

"Please, no more, Master William," John protested. "We'll have a sick filly on our hands."

So they denied Rachel any more sugar, but kept repeating her name, and walking her around the stableyard until she

had become accustomed to the sound as well as to the young
master who made it.

The next day both boys rode the pony separately and together, down the lanes near Larkbeare, and into Ottery St.
Mary, where William showed Joseph around the town, and
introduced his friend to the portly Dr. Cornish. The
minister admired Rachel with proper enthusiasm.

"I told the Major she would be just the filly for you." He
stroked her mane. "Had a streak of stubbornness in her
when she was a colt, but the Bentons broke her of it. Now
she's mild as her namesake in the Old Testament.
'Rachel' . . . "

"Yes, sir. Would you like to try her out?"

The stout clergyman's woolly white head shook back and
forth, while his massive middle shook up and down with
inward mirth. "My boy, I weigh more than you and Joseph
put together, and my bulk is not in the least adapted to
yearlings."

So they bade the rector good-day, and started home along
the Otter river, which wound on toward Larkbeare, whose
back lawns dipped down to its mossy banks. On the opposite
shore a grove of birch saplings shimmered and swayed in
the April breeze, like maidens flinging their newly-washed
hair in the sun to dry.

Carne's quick eye marked them at once. "Birch sapling
— just right for swinging! How can we get across?"

"There's the old boat on the pond, if John has put it in
condition. But first I promised to give Polly a ride on
Rachel when we came back," William reminded him.

"I'd forgotten," Joe said. "Now you see what it is to
have a little sister."

"I don't mind," William said good-naturedly. "We'll see
to the boat as soon as I'm done."

But after he had taken Polly around the park two or three

times, she insisted on following the boys to the pond to test the wobbly craft. "I want to come, too. If I stay here, Aunt Anne will have me practise on the pianoforte. Please, Billy!"

"Very well, just to the pond," William conceded. "But you can't cross the river with us."

The little boat, however, was still dilapidated and full of water from recent rains. John had had too much work getting the house and grounds in shape to fuss with caulking and painting.

"Bother, it's not been repaired!" William pushed the boat with his toe, but it only heaved dejectedly from side to side and sank lower.

"Now what do we do?" Carne asked.

"We could fix it ourselves. But we couldn't use it for a few days till the caulking sets."

"Isn't there a bridge across the river?"

"The nearest is at Ottery St. Mary. We could ride back, I suppose."

"Too far," Joe objected.

William suddenly brightened. "I say, why not let Rachel take us over?"

"You mean in the water?" Polly was wide-eyed.

"Certainly. Why not?"

"Of course, a capital idea, Bill!" Joe clapped him on the shoulder. He started for the pony and William followed.

"Wait." Polly put her hand shyly but firmly on William's arm. "The river is deep in the middle, John Goldsworthy says."

"Horses can swim." William was impatient to be off. "How do you suppose the cavalry fords a stream during the heat of battle?"

"Maybe Rachel doesn't like to swim."

"Nonsense!"

"You will get wet," Polly warned. "Better not go."

But the boys hardly heard her. They led Rachel to the bank, took off their bluchers and hose, rolled up their breeches, and climbed on the pony.

William lifted the reins. "Giddap!"

The pony stepped daintily into the shallows where the pebbles and sand shown through the clear water and the silver minnows darted from the path. The first cold shock caused Rachel to rear and stop dead. She did not enjoy the feeling. "Giddap," repeated William; but she would not budge.

He remembered what Dr. Cornish had said about her stubbornness. He reached in his pocket and found a piece of sugar. Leaning over and holding it just out of reach of her mouth in front of her, he coaxed, "Come, Rachel!"

The pony moved slowly forward. William dangled the sugar before her as long as he could, but then, with a complete thrust of her elastic lips, Rachel snagged the lump from his fingers and began to munch it. By this time they were nearly in the middle of the river, and the bottom sheered off suddenly. Rachel began to swim with the sure instinct of animals, but she objected to the load on her back. It was too heavy, and she was tired from her trip to Ottery St. Mary. With one quick lurch, she threw the boys from her back, and pitched them into the water.

It still held the winter's iciness, and was so unexpectedly cold they gasped and sputtered, floundering helplessly for some seconds before they could recover their wits. William had learned to swim at Fareham, where the salt sea buoyed him up with little effort on his part; but the fresh water in the river seemed loose and slippery. He felt himself sinking and fought to keep his head above the surface. Carne, too, was splashing furiously.

At last William regained his sense of balance, straightened

out and began to take long regular strokes, hissing to Joe, "Head for the home shore . . . it's closer . . ." The pony, meanwhile, had continued to cross the current and was already entering the shallows on the opposite shore, but the boys were too dashed to think about her.

Dripping, panting for breath, shivering and blue, they finally dragged themselves up on a short stretch of sand. As they lay resting silently, William saw John running along the bank as fast as his stubby legs would carry him.

"Hi — Master William: is it you, and Master Carne?" he called.

William lifted his head, feeling sheepish. "Yes, John."

"You're both alive, safe?"

"Yes."

The servant reached them, puffing from exertion and the fright he had suffered. "Thank the good Lord!" He took off his jacket which was oversized like his greatcoat in the winter, and bade the boys stand together so he could place it about the shoulders of both. "You ought to know better'n to make that pony cross the river this time of year, and loaded down with both of you," he scolded. "What did you want over there, I'd like to know! Why didn't you come and ask me?"

William eyed him suspiciously. "Did Polly tell you what we were going to do?"

"That little miss? No, indeed she didn't. I just happened to come down to trim the 'edge by the river, and the first thing I see is you and Master Carne, tumblin' into the brink, an' the filly takin' 'erself off . . ."

"Rachel!" William swung around and scanned the other side. "Did she get over? You don't suppose she drowned?"

"Don't worry. She's probably nibblin' sweet clover in the meadow this minute."

"We'd better bring her home somehow." William was worried. "Maybe she's strayed . . . "

"She can't have gone far," Joe put in. The boys huddled under the jacket, their teeth chattering, their skin puckered with goose pimples.

"I'll find 'er, never you mind." John Goldsworthy shoved them toward the house. "First thing is to get you dried and warm. Then I can take the mare, and go over the bridge in town to fetch Rachel back."

Reassured, the boys placed themselves in John's care. They knew he would find the pony. As a result of the chill they both took cold and were put to bed for a couple of days. William was glad Polly Graham had not peached to John or his mother about the enterprise. The boys watched her warily for some sign of triumph, but she did not even think of saying "I told you so." She was quiet and sympathetic, and brought them books to read, and chicken broth from Martha's kitchen. She followed Mrs. Carmichael-Smyth in and out of the room like a small shadow. When they returned to school and recounted their story, Carne would tell about her, too — what an annoyance, and what a brick she had been.

And thus he, William, was furnished with one more link with the others at Charterhouse: nearly all the boys had at least one small brother or sister to brag or complain about. It really was no family unless there were brothers and sisters in it. Mary Graham (Polly) was William's first cousin, and his mother's ward — as good as a sister. One by one the blocks that formed the foundation of his life, torn so early from under him, were being replaced, and the whole slowly strengthened.

Last Years at Charterhouse

After he became a day-boy, life at Charterhouse was easier for William. For one thing, he was more detached. When classes were over each day, he went to his room at Mrs. Boyes', where he was free to do as he chose until teatime. He could read, write to his mother or talk to his roommate when the other boy came from the Merchant Taylor's school next door. Or if he liked, he could do nothing but lounge.

And because he was away from the welter and tumult of boys, the clamor, insistence and push of so many hundreds of them all the time, the ache of trying to *belong* was not so great. It did not matter at all, in fact, that he might not care for sports, or hadn't a baronet in his family, or never cared to enter into the feuds, factions and intrigues that infested the halls of "Smiffle," nickname of Charterhouse. In the peace and comfort of his boardinghouse room, William felt a contentment he had never known at Penny's, and he wondered now why he had striven so desperately to become like the rest of the boys, to be one of them.

Moreover, he was one of the recognized champions ever since he had paid Tom Creighton out. And he was popular because he had not turned bully himself once he had won the battle. He was kind to the minors, the new boys and the less brawny. He was not a dictator. He remembered his own suffering, and had no desire to inflict it on others, as so many did when they got into power.

As a result, the little boys respected but did not fear him, and if the occasion arose, they did not hesitate to speak their minds. As a rule only the boldest dared enjoy this privilege, so "Thackeray" rapidly became among the most popular gownboys or students, and, in his last two years, he was known as the best-natured monitor.

Another reason for his greater happiness when he first went to the boardinghouse was that Richmond Shakespear enrolled at Charterhouse. His cousin was close at hand once more and they could go about together — to their Aunt Ritchie's, the theater at holiday-time, or now and then to visit the Thackeray relations in town. George Richmond was also at the school, and as the two brothers were together most of the time, Richmond and William were not quite the cronies they had been. Carne, Venables, Fawsett, Liddell, Freddy Boyes and Stoddard, his roommate, formed the greater part of William's circle. Nevertheless, he was pleased to have Rich nearby again.

On his trips to Larkbeare, William had had a chance for more outdoor activity, which increased his appetite. He ate such meals that his mother marvelled, and the Major looked on him with envy. He came back to school stout and broad-set, with cheeks rosy from the Devonshire air, and eyes that sparkled with health and good humor. His thick, curly hair more often than not went uncombed because he was lazy and didn't like to bother wrestling with the snarls from a night's sleep. Then his landlady would get after him, and scold and nag about his appearance till in desperation he combed his locks. Sometimes he wished Mrs. Boyes were not quite so motherly. But, in general, he was well satisfied with the new arrangement, enjoying his after-hours freedom from Dr. Russell's domain to the fullest.

He had stopped reading so many mysteries; they began to seem childish to him. He wondered how he could have spent hours lost in these imaginary castles, wandering with the hero through strange ways. He had discovered the essays of Addison and Steele, and found the brilliant, polished style more exciting than the adventures of errant heroes and blackhearted villains.

He did not discard the Waverley novels, however, as Walter Scott was too good a storyteller. He had brought "Ivanhoe" back from Larkbeare with him and was in the middle of reading it for the third or fourth time. He would have liked to go on with the tale as he slouched on the sofa in the student's parlor at Mrs. Boyes', his feet stretched toward the fire that took the chill from the fall day. Freddy Boyes was working a problem in Euclid, and William Stoddart, on the other end of the sofa, was leafing through the latest copy of "Blackwood's" magazine. A group of younger pupils played at jackstraws on the floor.

"Hooky," William said lazily to one of them, whose father was an earl, "go up and fetch me a volume of "Ivanhoe" out of my drawer, that's a good fellow."

From anyone else the request would have been a command, accompanied with a blow or threat to force immediate, cowering obedience, but since it was Thackeray, Hooky felt at liberty to ask, "Why don't you get it yourself?"

"Too far upstairs." William stretched out even farther, groaning as though he were overcome with fatigue. He said casually, "In the same drawer you will perhaps find a penny, which you may take for yourself."

Hooky jumped up. He had gained a penny in this way a few days ago. It was worth a trip to see if there was another lying in the drawer this time. He located the book without any trouble, but he could see no penny. He shuffled through a pile of papers, in the hope that one might be hidden by the disorderly stack. But the search was fruitless;

the drawer contained no coin. He picked up the copy of "Ivanhoe" and went downstairs. "Thackeray, you're a great snob," he said as he handed the book to William.

The only response to his thrust was an indulgent smile and a nod of thanks as William settled down to read. After he had completed a couple of chapters, he noticed that Stoddart had finished with "Blackwood's." He pounced on it before Freddy should get ahead of him. The boys also took the "New Monthly," the "London," and later on, the "Literary Gazette" when it was first published. There was always a rush for the new issues when they arrived each month, William's roommate usually winning out. The losers would scan the pages over his shoulder until he brushed them off, crying for privacy. "How can I read with all of you breathing down my neck? You can see it when I'm through."

"But you always lay hands on it before anyone else," William pointed out. "You've monopolized the privilege."

"It's up to you to move faster!" Stoddart liked to rib him about his indolence. "The only trouble is, you have to get up out of the chair, to see if the post has come. Ouch!" He dodged unsuccessfully as a book flung by William landed at his forehead.

The boys discussed the articles, when all had read them, arguing over the issues of the day. William's parents were both liberals, and William had lately become aware of the excitement in reforms: freedom of the press, the secret ballot, privileges for the farmer. These ideas, which in a few years were to flare into the burning issues that led to the Reform Bill, were just beginning to glimmer in the minds of thinking people. William, like his mother and stepfather, enjoyed being one of those who fanned the flame from the earliest spark.

On half-holidays, the boys sometimes went to the theater, to Astley's, which never failed to entertain them, or to an occasional play. Charles Matthews, the celebrated comedian, sent them into gales of laughter with his portrayal of a Frenchman, a performance which led to a good many imitations by William before an appreciative audience at the Ritchies'.

By this time the Ritchies had four children: besides William, who was nine, and Charlotte, six, there was another little girl, Jane, who was four, and a baby, John, just two years old. The apartment in Southampton Row bubbled and seethed with activity and noise, especially when the boys came from Charterhouse for the week end.

William frequently went to visit the Turners in Chiswick Mall from his own choosing these days. The schoolmaster had become even more imposing, but his daughters had grown into attractive, "amiable" young girls. After dinner, William would join his aunt and the "young ladies," as he liked to call his cousins, in a game of whist.

If the weather was fine, the pupils at Boyes' often went on fishing parties. William bought himself some fine new fishing tackle for five shillings, but he was hardly an expert or enthusiastic angler. He went on the angling parties because they were parties, and he was extremely sociable now that he was sure the others wanted his company. He liked the change of scenery, the green fields, the tea abroad instead of at home — there was an inn they used to stop at where one of his favorite kinds of cakes was served, but he rarely brought back any fish from these expeditions.

All these activities left him little time for schoolwork, which probably would have been entirely neglected if it had not been for Reverend Edward Churton. Mr. Churton, who assisted Dr. Russell with the written exercises of the upper school, was the only teacher in the school who seemed to show understanding toward the pupils and an interest in their individual tastes or problems.

He met the boys singly, one after another, in an anteroom. William was struck by the difference between him and Mr. Penny at their opening conference.

"Come in, Thackeray." The teacher had nodded pleasantly and picked up William's exercise sheets from a pile on his desk. He was already prepared with neatly written criticisms and corrections. "Just sit down and make yourself comfortable." (Penny or the Doctor would have let him stand, shifting from foot to foot.) "I find a portion of your work surprisingly good — and part of it incredibly bad. But most of your mistakes are due to carelessness. See here . . ." He leaned toward William to point out various corrections. "You can look these over thoroughly by yourself. What are you most interested in, Thackeray?"

William considered. He had never given the matter any thought. It was all "schoolwork," lumped together as a chore. "I suppose I prefer composition most of all, sir," he said at last. "I wouldn't mind writing an essay every day. Drawing comes next, but I do that all the time . . ."

"I know," Churton interrupted with an amused smile. "To the detriment of other work. What next?"

"I like history; I want to find out what men did in bygone days, what they thought, felt and wore, how they acted, what made great battles, heroes and conquerors." William paused. He had never spoken so much at length to a teacher. He considered again, and went on, "Mathematics is a monster; it makes my head swim. Latin transcriptions take too much time. And Greek, Greek is the worst of all."

"Why is that?"

"I don't know — maybe because we started with the verb,'I

thrash'..." It seemed a senseless thing to say, but the words came suddenly, and he somehow felt that his aversion to the classical language lay in the manner with which Dr. Russell began the course, hammering the brutal "I thrash!" into beginners' heads.

"I see." Mr. Churton nodded as though the feeling were quite natural. "It may be difficult for you to believe, William, but there's a great deal of beauty in Greek. Some day, if you stop worrying about Dr. Russell, you may be able to find it. And try reading the odes of Horace for the story. Then your Latin assignments won't seem a waste of time." He said it gently, adding a few verses from memory by way of illustration, for he was crammed to his fingertips with classical knowledge, yet what he said went through to a boy's understanding and stayed there. He placed a forcefulness beneath his words that made the listener respect them.

As the weeks went by, William respected the senior instructor more and more. There was a concealed power about Mr. Churton which most of the boys sensed and revered. He was invariably kind to small boys, but merciless to fools and braggarts. He was unexpectedly strong. Once during a boat-race he hit out with a stroke so rapid it astonished both the boys and the bargemen. In short, Churton was a "prince," the boys agreed.

But all the goodness and strength of character this noble professor displayed could not make up, in William's mind, for the vulgarity and meanness of Dr. Russell. In spite of everything Mr. Churton could say in praise of classical languages, William continued to hate his Latin and Greek because Dr. Russell taught them, and he hated the Headmaster, hated and dreaded and despised him all at the same time.

It seemed to him that the doctor took special delight in

picking on him, making him the butt of coarse, sarcastic jokes. William had only to open his mouth in translation, and the Doctor would pounce on him. "Thackeray, you are an idle, shuffling boy. It is a miracle that one boy should have so large a head, all crammed full of stupidity and dullness. Is this what your parents send you to school for, sir, to mock them with idleness and indolence?" He glared and went on and on. His tirades were rocket-like displays of temper, fascinating to those who were not the target of them, and extinguished with eclipse-like suddenness by the next recitation if it were a faultless one or if it came from one of the Headmaster's favorites.

Of course it was true that William was seldom prepared. Or if he were, in halfhearted fashion, he was not paying attention when Dr. Russell called on him to recite.

Henry Liddell sat next to him, and usually heard William's name called first. "Thackeray!" A stage whisper, and a sharp nudge in William's rib.

"Hmm? What?" William had to bring his wits back to the classroom with an effort.

"He called on you!" Still in a whisper.

"Oh. — Oh! Where's the place?"

"Line five, page two-ten." Or whatever it might be. William never had the place.

Then he would begin to translate, haltingly, with promptings from Henry here and there. Once in a while he got through passably well, but as a rule the Doctor interrupted him before he was barely started, to berate him for his work with cutting gibes and insults. The Headmaster's attitude took away any desire he might have to discover the beauties of which Mr. Churton spoke.

The older William grew, the more impatient the Doctor

became. Toward the end of his third year at Mrs. Boyes',
when he began to think and study in earnest because he
wished to enter Cambridge the following term, Dr. Russell
was unbearable toward him. Though he didn't like to
burden his mother, he couldn't help writing of the treatment
he received.

Dr. Russell is treating me every day with such mani-
fest unkindness and injustice that I really can scarcely bear
it [he wrote to her one dark, cold twilight during February].
It is hard, when you are endeavoring to work hard, to find
your attempts nipped in the bud — if ever I get a respectable
place in my form, he is sure to bring me down again; today
there was such a flagrant instance of it that it was the general
talk of school. I wish I could take leave of him tomorrow.
He will have this to satisfy himself with, that he has thrown
every possible object in my way to prevent my exerting
myself.

He flung down the quill, and sat in a frowning study for
some moments. If only he did not become so easily embarrassed by the doctor's insults! He always had to bite his
lips to keep the tears back, while his schoolfellows tittered in
appreciation of the teacher's acid wit. Many of them might
be in sympathy with him, but out of force of habit, or because they too were nervous before the Headmaster, or because it was politic to laugh at Dr. Russell's "cleverness,"
they giggled and sputtered, and their noises only made him
more uncomfortable. He considered the attacks particularly
unjust because now that he was older he prepared his assignments. He knew most of the odes of Horace by heart; but
he made little mistakes, like translating "the" as "and,"
which, small as it was, caused the axe to fall. Today a perfect
lesson had been spoiled by one such mistake, and he had
gone to the foot of the class! He sat with his chin in his
hands, and looked out gloomily at the trees in Charterhouse
Square, blurred and shadowy in the gloaming.

A knock at the door made him turn. "Come in," he said tonelessly.

It was George Venables. "Churton sent me over to Dr. Russell's with a message, and on the way back I thought I would see what you were doing." He rubbed his hands together. "Where's your fire? And why are you sitting in the dark?"

William rose and lit the candles, and dropped a flame on the sticks in the fireplace. "I've been giving my mother a picture of the ogre. I wonder you came away alive, George!"

"His bark is worse than his bite, you know." George took off his coat and muffler and lounged on the bed. "Though I will admit he was a pig to you today. Everyone said so. We were talking about it in the long-room."

"I'm glad I had your sympathies, at any rate." William's laugh was hardly mirthful. "I wish Dr. Russell could know the way the boys feel!" he went on heatedly. "If he saw how unpopular his dealings make him, perhaps he would be more fair."

George stretched himself full length across the bed. "We need the opinions of the pupils publicly aired, all right."

"If I had a magazine like "Blackwood's," I'd write a burning editorial on the abuses of headmasters," William said vehemently. "I'd tell them all . . ." He broke off suddenly. "I say, what about starting a school paper?" His eyes lit up at the thought of it. He jumped off the stool by his desk, and stood over George, shaking the other's shoulder.

"A school paper? What would we put in it?"

"Oh, I don't know — poems, essays, news, editorials," William counted them off on his fingers.

"You'd jolly well better not print editorials against the Doctor, or you won't have any paper," George warned him.

"I don't care about that part of it," William had pushed

his grievances to one side in his enthusiasm. "But think of starting a newspaper at Charterhouse. We'll become a force for boarding school reforms in time. We'll be famous!" He was carried away with bright dreams, dreams that were to be realized at a far distant date, when he wrote about his school in many of his books.

George sat up. "It might not be a bad idea, after all. What shall we call our paper?" He was ready to share ownership.

The matter required thought. Different titles came to mind, but they finally decided they would call the publication, "The Carthusian."

George noticed suddenly that it had grown completely dark, and he would be late delivering Dr. Russell's answer to Churton. "We'll work on the paper tomorrow after class," he promised, throwing on his coat and ducking out of the door.

All afire with his project, William set himself to writing verses that very night after tea. He wrote two or three pronounced "tolerable" by his roommate, Stoddart, who was inclined to be somewhat critical, and "excellent" by Venables the next day, when they met to discuss ways and means of getting the magazine circulated through the school.

Satires were popular, and William penned one called "Cabbages" on a precious poem of the day entitled "Violets." The author, Letitia Landon, would have been shocked if she had seen the sport "Cabbages" made of "Violets." He also turned out a little stanza designed to demonstrate cockney diction:

> In the romantic little town of Highbury
> My father kept a circulating library;
> He followed in his youth that man immortal, who
> Conquered the Frenchmen on the plains of Waterloo.
> Mama was an inhabitant of Drogheda,
> Very good to darn and embroider.

In the famous island of Jamaica,
For thirty years I've been a sugar-baker.
And here I sit, the Muses' 'appy vot'ry,
A-cultivatin' every kind of po'try.

His colleagues enjoyed a good laugh over this piece of tom-foolery. But though he and George Venables worked to compile the first issue, they couldn't find others who were interested, and the venture lagged. " 'The Carthusian' does not come on at all," William informed his mother sadly. "They seemed to have dropped all idea of it."

In spite of their plans, no issue was ever published. Dr. Russell grew more and more insulting, and in February William's parents decided he need not remain at Charter-house when the term was over late in May. The decision was a joyful one to William; he counted the days till the Long Quarter was through. "I feel every day as if one link were taken from my chain," he said in one of his letters. "I have consolation in thinking there are not many links more."

But from Dr. Russell, the news that he was leaving brought only more invectives heaped upon William. The Headmaster added another adjective when he began his customary tirade. "You are an idle, profligate, shuffling boy," he would begin. Then he would go on, "because your friends are going to take you away in May," etc., etc. He was especially bitter when anyone left the school. The number of students was down to half of what it had been.

"On every possible occasion, he shouts out reproaches against me for leaving his precious school, forsooth," William sneered. "There are but three hundred and seventy in the school, and I wish there were only three hundred and sixty-nine."

After "The Carthusian" dropped away, his sole solace for the remaining time was a half-holiday or week end spent at

Southampton Row. One Saturday night he was there for dinner with Richmond, and in the evening they went to the Adelphi theater where they saw Elizabeth Yates, who was appearing in comedy all season. How delightful the play was, how charming the actress! He was transported to another world and lost there till the curtain came down on the final act.

He longed to cut Dr. Russell's lectures and go to Town for the performance the very next day, but he knew he would pay for it with extra coals heaped upon him from the professor's fire. If the miserable term would ever end! He had frequent headaches, but he continued to attend classes to avoid controversy.

But a morning came when his headache was so intense he couldn't get out of bed, and he was burning with fever. Mrs. Boyes sent for the physician, who pronounced William a very sick lad.

Three weeks later, still weak from his illness, before the long term of 1828 had ended, he left Charterhouse for good. He thought he would be happy never to see its hateful halls again.

12

Interlude at Larkbeare

He had been home only a few days when the fever sent him to bed once more. His room swam in front of his eyes, its objects taking on the contorted and unreal shapes of figurines in a goldfish bowl, seen through the shimmering transparencies of water and glass. The caricatures he had drawn for the walls jumped from their frames alive — tiny little gnomes, who pranced along the wall and up and down the green stuff drapes. They never stopped dancing before his blurred vision. For three days now his fever had been raging, and the leeches on his forehead, sucking out the blood to make his temperature go down, only caused him to feel weaker, giddier.

The one thing that appeared real was his mother's cool hand resting on his brow with the gentleness of a rose petal. "How is it, William?" She had just tiptoed into the room, followed by the physician, who, in turn, had Polly Graham in his wake, some paces behind. "Feeling better?"

He shook his head, closing his eyes to enjoy fully the cool softness.

The physician was more brusque than Mrs. Carmichael-Smyth. "Let me take a look at the patient, please, Madam." He put William's mother to one side, and bent over the bed. "The leeches are bringing on feebleness. We will remove them for a day or so." He began to pry away the small black insects, while William grimaced to show how much he disliked the process.

What a bother to be sick! The helplessness, the weakness

and wild fancy in his brain drove him mad. There were moments when he thought he would rather return to Dr. Russell's wrath than suffer this illness.

But after three more weeks the fever began to abate, and finally burned itself out. He awoke one morning to find the furniture back in focus again, his caricatures returned to their normal places, and his books to neat rows of volumes on the shelves instead of indistinct masses blocked against the wall. He noticed Mary Graham for the first time, coming in meekly behind his mother, who was bringing in his breakfast tray.

"Hello, Polly. Don't you think it's time I took another plunge in the river? How is Rachel?" He tried to seem well and strong.

"You know me, you *do* know me, Billy! Aunt Anne, he sees me, he's well!"

"Thank God!" Mrs. Carmichael-Smyth, setting the tray on the bed, fell on her knees and uttered a prayer of gratitude. Deeply religious, she often gave vent to her feelings this way.

William watched her in some surprise. "Come, mother, I wasn't so sick, was I? You sound as if I had been snatched from the grim Reaper himself." It was an effort to talk, but he had to joke.

"Hush, William, you must not make light of your illness. There were days when I thought you were . . . were . . ." Here she broke down in tears. The relief from strain was too much.

"Poor mother. I'm sorry to be such a trouble to you. But what have you on the tray? Uncover the dishes, Poll. I think I'm hungry!"

His cousin delightedly took the lid from a bowl of gruel and removed the napkin from some toast, while his mother poured a cup of tea. It was the first food he had tasted for days. His mother found great pleasure in carrying an empty tray downstairs at last.

After she and Mary had gone, William lay back exhausted and slept again for several hours. He gained strength rapidly from then on, though the doctor kept him in bed a few weeks more, until all danger of another relapse was past. He ate enormously of chicken and jellies and puddings sent up to him by Martha Goldsworthy, who was determined to "fatten the young man up." And when he grew restless of being confined to his room, the doctor pronounced him ready to leave it.

He dressed slowly the first day, John helping him get into his clothes. He was more shaky than he had expected.

"Wait till you see Rachel, sir," John said. "She's a stout mare, grown almost as broad as you have tall."

At the man's words, William realized that when he stood up, he was looking down at the servant from quite a distance. Was it a trick of his illness? He strode to the pier glass across the room.

The image that confronted him was familiar — the large head, the broken nose, the mild eyes — but the body was elongated by a great many inches, as if it had been stretched out of proportion in a convex mirror. He blinked and stared again; moved backward, and forward. He remained the same: he was over six feet tall, well over.

"John, I've become a giant! I must have had 'growing' sickness!" He continued to marvel while the man buttoned his waistcoat, adjusted his frill, and tied a white kerchief around his neck. "Do you know I was only five-six when I went to bed, and now I'll wager I'm six-two."

"You've become a man, sir." John viewed him with pride. "A week or two and you'll be sixteen. There aren't many over six feet at your age."

William had, as a matter of fact, attained the unbelievable height of six feet, three inches during his weeks in bed. His stepfather, who laughed a great deal over the way Bill had to look down at everyone in the household, measured his height with the tape from Mrs. Carmichael-Smyth's work basket. William's mother thrilled with joy over her tall son, and Polly Graham regarded him with positive awe. She was a quiet little thing anyhow, and now that her cousin, in one jump, had become a man, she felt strange and shy with him.

For his part, William was amused and uncomfortable. In many ways he still thought of himself as a gownboy. He didn't feel grown up inside in the least. He was still insecure and unsure of himself, inexperienced in worldly matters, yet this great, hulking figure of a man confronted him when he looked in the mirror. Furthermore Polly treated him as if he were years older, as if he knew all that men know, and should act like them.

He saw her coming through the green door in the wall one day when he was in the yard getting ready to mount Rachel. "You're just in time, Polly. I'm off for Ottery St. Mary. I have room for one passenger. Would you like to go?" He patted the saddle.

"If you care to take me, William."

" 'William?' Oh, I say, come off it, Poll. If you are going to be so formal, please make it William Makepeace. I have no patience with halfway measures."

"It's only . . . because you're a man now."

"Nonsense. I'm merely taller. Make up your mind!"

"All right, Bill." His impatience convinced her and she smiled suddenly. "I'd like to go along."

"Good girl!" He hoisted her up.

With the air cleared on this point, William and his little cousin became good friends again. They went fishing together as well as riding, and in the evening, Polly and Mrs. Carmichael-Smyth would play duets after dinner while the Major and William listened.

It was a leisurely summer. William read his books twice over, and went to Dr. Cornish for more. "Are you reading for college or for pleasure?" he asked as he led the way into the library.

"Both!"

"I see." The doctor nodded his white head approvingly. "Where do you plan to go?"

"Cambridge, I think, sir. Stoddart, my roommate, has gone to Oxford, and wants me to join him, but Carne and Venables and some of my cronies at Charterhouse are at Cambridge, and the Major seems to favor it."

"Are you going to study for the cloth?"

"Oh, no, sir! At least, I never thought of it. I haven't decided what I shall do yet. I shall have my patrimony when I am twenty-one. My father left me a fair-sized inheritance. I may be able to live on it comfortably."

"Never plan on what may fall to your lot without effort, my son," Dr. Cornish warned. He picked various volumes off the shelves, and William went away with an armload of them, as well as plenty of advice on the clergy as an honorable, rewarding profession.

But though many Charterhouse boys planned to enter the church, William had no desire to do so. He was still too gaunt and frail to enter college when autumn came, so the Major offered to help him to prepare for midyear entrance in February.

"It has been a good many years since I entered Trinity, but a military man does not forget his mathematics," he said. "We shall see how much of Euclid comes back to me."

He proved to be a patient teacher, and William was

amazed to find himself "galloping through Euclid." He found, too, that he enjoyed the study hours alone with his stepfather, and a camaraderie never apparent before developed between them. They conversed and joked between problems. They took wine together after dinner, when the Major discussed politics with him as man to man.

He had never spent so long a period at home, and its inmates became progressively dear to him as the months passed. His mother was so like a royal court lady. Late in December they all went to a concert in Sidmouth, and he was struck once again with her beauty and regal bearing. She entered the hall on the arm of the Major after William and Polly were seated. Vivid in black velvet, her only ornament a medallion at her white throat, she attracted all eyes in the audience.

"How magnificent my mother is!" he breathed, more to himself than Polly. He watched Mrs. Carmichael-Smyth move down the aisle . . . "like a duchess."

13

A Sentimental Journey

IN FEBRUARY, when it was time for William to go to Cambridge, the Major proposed to accompany him, seeing old haunts en route. "We'll stop in London a few days; visit Charterhouse . . ."

"Thank you, I don't think I care to stop there!" William interrupted him. "My school memories are none too pleasant!"

The Major merely smiled and made no comment. But on February 23 they stood before the Charterhouse gates. A moment later, in spite of certain misgivings, William walked onto the Green, a thrill actually running through him at the sight of old landmarks.

"That's where the bully, Creighton, struck me when my nose was healing." He pointed to the spot. "And here's where I paid him out!" William stopped to relive his triumph. "The boys play marbles or roll their hoops here, and over there they drag you into a cricket match." He chuckled suddenly. "But just around the corner is the pastrycook's, and Carne and I used to sneak away . . ."

At this point in his memories, the bell rang for midday, and the boys came pouring out of class. It took those who knew him a minute to realize that the tall young gentleman in a rakish new suit of the latest cut was "old Thackeray," but John Leech recognized him because of his shout of laughter as he saw the pupils break into a dozen different fights, squabbles, bargainings, games and other odd pursuits on their way to the mess hall.

"Thackeray! It's Bill Thackeray!" John rushed toward him. "I say, you *are* a swell!" he said admiringly as they shook hands.

"Not quite. I'm just on my way to Cambridge. Hello, Fawsett!" This to the youngest of the Fawsetts, who had been called "minimus" until the past year. "Hello, Browne, Montgomery, Gatty." He shook hands with a score of boys. "You all remember my governor, I think." The Major bowed, nodded and greeted the boys with his usual kindliness. "How is Mr. Penny? And Churton? and . . . " William hesitated, for just then a professor emerged from the door rather absent-mindedly adjusting his spectacles to see why such a crowd had gathered, the Latin Grammar he held nearly slipping from his grasp.

William stared once, and once again. Could this little man approaching them be — no, it couldn't — but it was! Dr. Russell. Was he always so commonplace in appearance? Or was it because William now stood much taller than the Doctor? He had been gone only eight months, but the perspective had changed completely. The lion, the fierce eagle had vanished, and here was a small, simple man, saying, "What is going on, gentlemen? Proceed to . . . "

"Good-day, Dr. Russell." William went up to the Headmaster and held out his hand. He couldn't help smiling as he recognized the Latin Grammar as the very one that had so often boxed his ears.

"Well, bless my soul, it's Thackeray!" cried the Doctor, grasping William warmly. "What a distinguished gentleman you have become. How do you do, Major Carmichael-Smyth? You gentlemen will do me the honor of having lunch, of course? Browne, give my compliments to Mr. Penny and Mr. Churton, and ask them to my apartment for lunch."

As the boy ran off to do his bidding, the Doctor announced

to the playground in general: "A half-holiday, boys!" and a cheer went up. The three then made their way to the Doctor's study, once so fearful, now so harmless. The Headmaster opened what William had always thought was a cabinet of classics, but was revealed as a container for claret. The "volumes" were only painted on the outside: inside was a decanter and a circle of wineglasses! Amazed as he was, William could scarcely keep his face straight as the Doctor handed him his claret. If only he had known such secrets as this a few months before!

They took their meal with Mrs. Russell, Penny and Churton in the Doctor's private dining-room. It was good to talk with Mr. Churton, and Mr. Penny's lips did not seem nearly so huge, though he appeared by comparison more of an ass than before .

Later William joined the boys again, and treated a crowd of them to tarts at the pastrycook's, as any true "old boy" ought to do when he returns to his school. It gave him a sensation of grandeur, swaggering across the Green with a parcel of lads surrounding him. When he and the Major finally left for their hotel, it was with the heartiest farewells, and promises to return.

"Good old Charterhouse!" William murmured dreamily as they drove away in the cab. "How different it is when you're no longer a pupil! I wouldn't have believed I could feel this way."

"I rather thought you might enjoy going back," was all the Major said, but his eyes crinkled slightly at the corners.

Slaughter's Coffee House, St. Martin's Lane, where they were to stay, had been a favorite haunt of artists since the time of Hogarth. William, who admired the great caricaturist, thought it odd that this meeting-place of artists should be quite ordinary in appearance. "The coffee house with the murderous name," he called it.

The Major laughed. "Ah, but they have magnificent roast sirloins of beef. I shall order one for our dinner. Then what do you say to the evening performance at the Adelphi?"

"Yes, yes! First, last and always!" William agreed.

The next afternoon, as the Major was dining with a military friend, William went alone to Southampton Row, where, with very little effort on the part of his cousins and Aunt Ritchie, he was persuaded to stay for dinner. His uncle, Frank Thackeray, who lived in Grosvenor Place, was also to dine.

"He will probably have a name or two in the family to give you," Mrs. Ritchie said. "And I have written a letter for you to Dr. George Thackeray, Provost of King's College."

"Provost of King's! What illustrious relatives I have. How shall I be able to face them?"

"You will do very well." His aunt looked at him fondly. Her big, sweet face and motherly figure had changed very little in the ten years that William had been coming to visit in Southampton Row. Only the laugh lines around her mouth had deepened a trifle. "To think little Billy-boy is entering Cambridge!" she marvelled.

It was so ridiculous they all shouted. William Ritchie, now eleven, reached up to pat his cousin's head. "Yes, our dear Gargantua!" While Charlotte reproved her mother with, "Oh, Mamma!"

But William, laughing, kissed his aunt, and thought how much he loved her.

14

"Keeping" at Cambridge

THE SERVANT or "gyp" who showed the Major and William to his rooms on the ground floor in the Great Court, Trinity College, pointed out in passing, "There's the Master's Lodge, sir, and just across, on the left of the Great Gate, is your door. Here we are! The apartment above this is where Newton kept, you know," he added impressively as he turned the key in the lock.

"Isaac Newton — where?"

"The windows overhead, sir. 'E like the tower to work in; 'ad 's hinstruments there, they say." The gyp opened the outer door of heavy oak, and then the inner one to the apartment. "I think you'll find everything in order, sir. I shall be round in the morning to get you up and straighten the place a bit. Anything either of you gentlemen 'd like before I go?"

"No, no, it's all very good." William crossed the front living or study room, and opened the bedroom door as he spoke. The rooms, though not particularly attractive, were neat. He could have them redecorated later. The Major tipped the servant, and the man, after dropping a lighted taper on the logs in the fireplace, left them.

William opened one of the windows and leaned out toward the tower. "You heard him, governor; Newton lived in that tower. I shall send my mother a sketch, and mark the spot. Perhaps by living in the shadow of greatness, I shall become great. Men will say some day that Newton and Thackeray "kept" near one another, as my trusty gyp saith!"

He had been in Cambridge only twenty-four hours, but like all freshmen, he was eager to show his familiarity with its customs, its landmarks, and its slang. He felt extravagant, reckless. Excitement beat high within him at the thought of being part of the illustrious fame that was Cambridge history, and at the thought of the new, free life he was to lead — a young man of the world, with his "rooms," his "gyp," his supply of sauterne with which he would entertain his friends. And if there lurked a quiver of uncertainty in these sensations, it only added to the air of boldness. "I shall be known from Trinity to Caius; from King's to Corpus Christi." He counted off dramatically on his fingers some of the colleges of Cambridge.

"It requires a vast deal more than living in the shadow of the great to become one of them," the Major remarked to him drily. "You might begin by considering the reading course Mr. Whewell laid out for you."

William Whewell was the tutor or fellow of Trinity College in charge of "reading" students, those working for a degree. The Major had written to him from London, sending William's compliments along with his own, and they had had a conference with him shortly after arriving in Cambridge the previous day. He was a distant, dried-up sort of man who had little time to give much attention to his tutees outside of recommending a reading outline. If they needed instruction, he suggested a private tutor, one of the graduate students who needed money while working for fellowships.

"Oh, yes . . . " William settled down abruptly. "And I must look up that Senior wrangler, Mr. Fawcett, whose card Mr. Whewell gave me. Let's see, where is it?" He began hunting in his waistcoat pockets. "Don't worry, my dear Pa, I shan't be afraid to work once I get started!"

The Major, reassured, clapped him on the shoulder fondly. "I know you won't, my son. Be as gay as you wish for the present."

But William's spirits were considerably lower the next morning, after he had seen Major Carmichael-Smyth off in the coach, and returned to his rooms alone. The apartment seemed quite empty without his stepfather's kindly presence. It was nine-ten by his gold watch — just too late for lecture. The gyp had brought his trunks up, and he set about putting his things away. The buckish, blue-black coat with velvet collar, which he had ordered in London, had arrived, too. He tried it on. A neat fit, and stylish, he felt. He wished there were a longer glass than the one in the wardrobe. At any rate, he would be as well dressed as any Cambridge pensioner. The majority of students were pensioners, or middle class. Below them were the "sizars," poorer students, and above them were noblemen and fellow-commoners.

His clothes finally put away, William nailed up some small shelves he had brought along, hung the caricatures from his walls at Larkbeare, set his parents' miniatures on his bedside table, hung a scarf Polly had given him over the table in the study, and busied himself all morning to chase away his loneliness.

It was one o'clock when he finished. What to do next? He wished his boxes of books had come from Larkbeare so he could fill the cases. But he wished more ardently for company. He had called on Carne the day before, but Joe's gyp said his young man was out of town and would not be back till late afternoon. Then he had run into James Hine, a Merchant Taylor man Stoddart had introduced him to at Mrs. Boyes'. Hine was of Corpus Christi; he had invited William to call on him any time. Why not today? William thought as he sat aimlessly staring around his rooms in search of some little duty he might have overlooked. There was nothing more to be done; the place could stand no more fixing up. . . .

Hine was very cordial. "Come in, Thackeray, come in!" He put aside a volume of Plato's "Republic," and offered William a pipe from the row that stood on the desk. "Smoke?"

"No, thank you, not just now." William had not taken up the habit of tobacco yet. "I made good use of your invitation, you see, but I don't want to disturb you in the midst of such commendable labor." He picked up the book.

"Oh." Hine seemed embarrassed. "I'm only making a feeble try. If I were really serious I'd have been sporting my oak, you know." Seeing that William was puzzled, he explained: "Had the outer door closed, in other words — that's our 'do not disturb' sign here."

"I see. I daresay I shall be sporting *my* oak once I start reading," William nodded wisely. "But just now I am at a loss for occupation of any sort."

"I think you should become acquainted with your surroundings first of all," Hine said. "Come, I shall act as guide."

They went out and walked among the groves and fields bordering the colleges of Cambridge — King's, Trinity, Corpus and the rest — Hine talking all the while of university life, and William listened with both his ears so that any circumstance might find him prepared.

"You really should attend the boat race at Chesterton this afternoon," Hine said. "It is the duty of all undergrads to go, and follow the boats back to Cambridge on shore, to cheer your college to victory."

As he spoke they were approaching the quadrangle at

Caius, and William found a familiar face for the second time. James Young, a Charterhouse crony who had left school a year before William, came rushing up to them.

"I say, it's Bill Thackeray, am I right?" he pumped William's hand up and down.

"Right, Jim, old boy, how are you?"

"Capital, couldn't be better. What's your college?"

"Trinity. You're Caius?"

Young nodded. William introduced him to Hine and he proffered, "I'm off to the boat races at Chesterton this minute. Come with me, you two, and try to shout me down."

Hine had a conference with his tutor and could not, but William walked the two miles to the spot where the race was to start. A thousand noisy "gownsmen" were milling around on the bank, talking, laughing, laying private bets on the college most likely to win, and yelling to cronies among the crews of the boats lined up across the water.

A sharp report of the starting gun, and they were off, a thousand frantic gownsmen following on the run, with cheers as loud as their lusty lungs would permit. James Young and William joined in the din: "Hail, Caius!" "On, Trinity, on!"

Even with his gangley legs, William had to sprint to keep up with the rowers. They took the rapid strokes with clock-like precision, moving down the river with lightning speed. Now one boat would be in the lead, then another shot forward to take its place, accompanied by frantic huzzahs from its particular constituents.

A mile of such a pace was all that William could manage. "I — say, — Young, can't we — surrender?" he panted, stopping to rest. "Perhaps Trinity or Caius will win without us."

"Never!" his companion insisted diabolically. "But we might slow down, just a bit," he conceded shortly after.

Before long they had slowed to a walk, and reached the finish line as the crowd was dispersing and the boats being carried to lockers on the shoulders of their crews. Neither Trinity nor Caius but Corpus Christi had won the day.

"We might have known Corpus would be the victor," William said; "just because Hine didn't come!"

The race over, it was dinner time, so they went to Hall, an immense dining room filled with long tables at which the students wasted no time seating themselves. Like the rest of the men, William devoured a vast dinner, meat, cabbage, bread, pudding, but he thought privately that the beef was bad.

After dinner, he went to his rooms and donned his new surplice and cap, preparatory to attending chapel. The cap suited him very well, he thought, as he took it off and hung it on one of the pegs in the vestry before entering the church. But when he came out to fetch it at the close of chapel, his new head-covering had disappeared, and an old, greasy, ragged one was hanging in its place!

He stared down at it, puzzled and angry. Who would commit a deed like this? Snatch a brand new cap, and leave this wretched thing in its stead? He was ready to attack the nearest man, but the caps all looked alike, varying only in degrees of age. Then suddenly he laughed: Hine had told him to beware of tricks which might be played on him the first few weeks. So this was a sample. Well, he would not, at least, swallow the bait all the way, and make a great fuss, only to have them all claim innocence. He clapped the miserable substitute on his head, and sauntered carelessly out of chapel.

He had left a note for Joseph Carne, including an invitation to come to his rooms for tea, and had asked Hine to join them. He hurried home to prepare for his friends. Just as he put the kettle on the hob over the fire, there was a banging on the knocker, and, without waiting for him to open, Joe walked in.

"Bill! My dear old Thack! You've finally come to Cambridge. Now we shall have some high times!" Carne's bright manner, his bright brown hair and eyes had become even more pronounced. He was a dashing sophomore.

"It's good to see you, Joe." William pushed forward the most comfortable chair the room offered. "Charterhouse lost what little luster it held when you left."

"Charterhouse! How was it last year?" Joe asked.

"Pretty grim. When I left the mere thought of it was enough to make me vomit. But when we stopped there last week, it wasn't so dreadful, do you know?"

"Oh, you exaggerated its faults and overlooked its virtues as a school! We had plenty of good times there, too. Do you remember . . . " And Joe was off on a spree of reminiscences.

James Hine joined them a short while later, and they made tea and toasted thick slices of bread on long forks over the fire. It was late when the two callers left, Joe promising to arrange a party for a bunch of Charterhouse men sometime the following week. There was only time for a short note to his mother before William went to bed.

His first day at Cambridge was over, a pleasant, leisurely, entertaining day, free from supervision, and full of friendliness. As he settled himself for the night, he suddenly recalled his first day at Charterhouse, and the miserable, lonely creature he was that night. Most of the hostile faces then were the cronies he hailed with such delight now. At Cambridge there was no Dr. Russell, no birch rod, no particular regulation, no awful Authority hanging over you. You were considered a man; yes, a man, capable of making your own decisions, of forming your own opinions.

The next week he met his private tutor, Henry Edward Fawcett, who had been a wrangler, or senior honor student, at Trinity the year before. Studious in appearance, he was every inch "a reading character," who set about coaching William in algebra at their opening conference. Besides mathematics, they were to read the classics together. They were to have daily sessions from six to seven, with classics and mathematics alternately.

There were a great many Thackeray relatives to call upon in Cambridge, more than William had expected. In addition to the Provost of King's, Dr. George Thackeray, there was Dr. Frederic Thackeray, a physician, who offered to treat William when he needed medical attention. There was his mother, Mrs. Thomas Thackeray, who, because of the number of physicians in her family (another son was a famous doctor in Bath) enjoyed talking of nothing so much as fevers and deaths, with which she plagued William for one whole evening, but she redeemed herself by saying she loved the name of Thackeray. (William, too, loved it for some reason he could not explain. Fond as he was of his stepfather, he would never care to assume the name of Carmichael-Smyth.)

The evening was further redeemed by his meeting Martin Thackeray, Vice-Provost of King's. William decided almost immediately that he liked the Vice-Provost better than the Provost, perhaps because Martin Thackeray asked him to dine at once. They made an engagement for the following Saturday.

The Vice-Provost's rooms in King's were the most elegant William had seen; he was sure they must be the finest in the university. Mr. Thackeray had asked some undergraduates of his acquaintance in to meet William, but only one of them was able to come, he said. That one was none other than Walter Fawsett of Charterhouse. William was delighted to see him, but Walter, thinking he must "talk elegant" in the presence of an important university Don like the Vice-Provost, would not unbend when he found his old schoolfellow was a relative of Mr. Thackeray.

He spoke about the climate of Cambridge. "The salubrity of the Cambridge air induces many valetudinarians to resort to it," he said in studied, scholarly accents.

William sputtered, nearly choked on the excellent hock his cousin had served them. "Salubrity," "valetudinarian," indeed — the ass.

Had he chosen to do so, William could have spent all his time among the members of his father's family at Cambridge. But, naturally, he preferred to find other companionship as well. He made the acquaintance of an older man, Albert Badger, who had matriculated at Trinity the fall before at thirty-two, an age when most men would be seasoned Masters. Badger made no secret of not having had the opportunity to attend the university when he was young, nor of the fact that he was burning with an ardent desire for knowledge. He put above all else the fact that he wanted to be a Greek scholar. Supper and wine parties and teas meant little to him. He inspired William to yearn for more honest study of the classics also, and they agreed to read Greek plays together.

Because of this and for reasons of convenience, William changed his schedule. His new one he outlined in a letter to his mother:

> I go to Fawcett every other morning from 8 to nine; to Fisher (the Math lecturer) from nine to ten; and to Hare (the classical one) from ten to eleven. Then with Badger from eleven to twelve; twelve to half past one. Euclid or Algebra, and an hour in the evening at some one or other

of the above or perhaps at some of the collateral reading connected with Thucydides or Aeschylus.

He and Badger pored over Greek plays more for pleasure than anything else, a motive so different from avoiding Dr. Russell's birch rod that William was led farther and farther in the study of the language. He began to see the beauties Reverend Churton had spoken of, though at the time he had not been able to believe that good master. To increase his appreciation, he determined to *think* in Greek when he read. How pleased Churton would be to know it!

As at Charterhouse, Joe Carne was William's greatest crony. The two saw each other nearly every day, though Carne's influence was not exactly in the direction of ancient classicism.

He burst in on William's preparation of Greek one early evening in March. "I'm on my way for a walk to Trumpington," he announced without apologizing for his failure to knock. "And you must come along, Thack. It's a fine night."

"A lot of good it does me to sport my oak," William grumbled. "I might as well leave both doors wide open!"

"You will go cross-eyed reading so much." Carne closed his friend's book and pulled him out of his chair. "Everyone needs a little fresh air now and then."

He did not have to coax long. William was only too ready for diversion when it came between him and study. He liked to read, but he could not resist the society of his friends. He stretched his long legs, rose, and put on his coat with the velvet collar. "Very well, vile tempter; let us proceed!" He clapped an arm about Carne's shoulder, and they went out into the starlit night.

Like most undergraduates, they plunged into deep intellectual waters, gave themselves authoritative critical powers

in matters of poetry and prose, and condemned or praised a
piece of writing with a fine assurance and highhandedness
characteristic of young college men. The philosophic sky
over Cambridge seemed to engender such an attitude.
Carne, who was particularly quick at catching the latest
trends of thought, gave out with his usual glibness as they
walked along the darkening streets. The current fashion in
Cambridge decreed that Byron was no great poet, though a
very clever man, a theme on which Joe held forth brilliantly
for some blocks, while William listened, smiling.

"There's a man next to me in Hall who aspires to write
verse," he said presently, during a lull in the flow of Carne's
discourse. "Rather a pleasant sort; name's Tennyson."

"Yes, his brothers Charles and Frederick published a
volume last year," Carne said, who knew all the facts. "The
one you mean, Alfred, is going to try for the prize poem this
year."

"What is the subject?" William was much interested.

"Historical — Timbuctoo."

"I think I'll try for it. Why not?"

"Why not, indeed? I may have a fling at the contest myself! Perhaps it will end in a draw. Who at Cambridge can
surpass Carne and Thackeray?"

They laughed and cheered each other and tossed their
caps in the air. Above their mild commotion, they suddenly
heard the sweet sound of a harpsichord issuing forth on the
night air from the house in front of them. A girl's voice
accompanied the music.

"Hush!" William admonished his friend. "Some fair
maid is singing 'The light, the light guitar.'"

It was the most popular song of the day, and they stopped
to listen a moment. Then, by unspoken but common consent, they walked slowly and silently under the window,

where they waited until the verse was finished. When the young lady arrived at the chorus, they opened their throats and joined the melody in full, ringing tones. William sang baritone, Joe tenor. They put their heads together to blend the harmony further, and wished for Walter Fawsett or James Young to carry the bass.

Halfway through the lines the door flew open! Who or what came out, neither one would ever know, for William fled towards Cambridge with all the speed his long legs were capable of, while Carne ran the other way. William did not stop till he reached the safety of his room, where he dropped panting into a chair, and roared aloud at the escapade, so that the man who "kept" across the hall rapped for quiet.

Wondering whether Joe made it to his rooms without being caught, William decided he had better make sure, and set out for Carne's. But his friend was sitting calmly over a cup of tea and a pipe, blowing great clouds of smoke into his little room. William joined him, and over the aromatic billows they talked of Shelley, Dr. Johnson and Pope. William had been reading "The Revolt of Islam," which prompted him to pass a great many remarks about Shelley's ideas in the poem.

"You sound as if you were ready for a speech on the subject," Joe observed. "Why don't you apply for election to the Union?"

William had considered becoming a member of this famous undergraduate debating society, but he stood rather in awe of a big organization like the Union. "I should never have the courage to rise," he confessed. "Are you able to stand and say your piece?"

"Of course! There's nothing to it," Joe claimed. "You rise, the Chair recognizes you, and you state some opinion, like those you voiced just now about Shelley. I get up at every meeting."

I don't doubt it, William smiled to himself.

"Shelley's to be the subject in a few weeks," Carne was still talking. "Do come into it, Thack!"

"Perhaps I shall. Now I must go home and get some sleep." William put down his pipe.

"Don't forget we are to ride to Wimpole Saturday," Joe reminded him. "And next week I am giving a supper party."

"Good." And William was off to his own domain.

His friend was always full of plans, and seemed to have a genius for creating anecdote. On the ride to Wimpole, the two cronies got lost. They rode six miles out of their course, and William was late for his tutor. Why did things usually happen in Carne's company? Perhaps because he was gay, idle, good-natured and not particularly deep. When William was elected to the Union a short time later, he realized how shallow Joe was. It was true that he stood up at every meeting, ready with an opinion no matter what the subject, but he spouted pure "flam," not a solid idea in all his reasoning. His remarks were scarcely taken seriously. William preferred to listen quietly rather than run the risk of being ridiculed in debate.

Nevertheless, he seldom refused Carne's invitations, and if his old schoolmate did not come to William's rooms, he went to Joe's. He stopped to pick up his friend for Lecture one morning, and just as they were leaving, Carne's washerwoman came up the steps, a huge straw hamper in her arms. She was pretty and plump, with rosy cheeks, and steamy curls straying out of her cap. Though she moved to one side, they could barely get past her, so big was the basket and so narrow the stair.

"Take care that you don't fall down, my pretty maid!" Joe said, tweaking one of her curls, and William, taking his cue from his friend, cried, "Indeed, she's pretty as Phyllis; and I shall be her Corydon!" And he gave her a smacking big kiss.

The washerwoman dropped her hamper and placed her hands on her hips, drawing herself up to full height. "I was never so insulted in my life!" she burst out, with a fierce glare at the culprit.

Lest her anger take on the more tangible form of the hamper hurled at their heads, the two rogues hurried down the steps and out into the street. Once the door was safely closed behind them, they cut a caper or two on the walk, and hummed "The Irish Washerwoman's Jig" all the way to lecture.

William bought a set of foils and tackle, which he put to good use by fencing nearly every day with Carne, Young, Fawsett or Moody. He was also busy with a number of other things. He continued to go to the Union debates, but he would not speak in public. He tried once, on the subject of Napoleon, but he was a dismal failure. Carne had just finished speaking in his usual easy, fluent manner, and then he, William, got up and stuck in the mud at his first footstep! He "blustered and blundered, and retracted, and stuttered," as he wrote his mother afterward. At last with one desperate sentence, "Napoleon as a Captain, a Lawgiver, and a King merited and received the esteem and gratitude of the French nation," he had "sat down like Lucifer never to rise again."

He started an essay club with three other Carthusians — Brome, Moody and Young. They decided, however, to ask no more Charterhouse men. Four was enough; any more would make it a clannish group. They planned eventually to try for a membership of ten since with that number they would scarcely have to write three essays a year, so it would not require much time.

He met with Young and Moody on April 16 to discuss the project, but his cronies spent more time talking about "the old days" at Charterhouse than the essay club — which was one of the reasons he would insist on outside members. There were so many interesting things to do at Cambridge besides hashing over old experiences! A sudden thought occurring to him, he sat down to write his daily journal to his parents:

> This day last year (as I just called to mind) did I leave Charterhouse. And now I am sitting at Cambridge writing a letter home with a mind perfectly contented with the change the year has wrought in my situation. I have just had two men here who from 8 to 12 have been talking over Old Charterhouse doings, telling for the hundredth time old Charterhouse stories which possessed but little interest at their first broaching, & a great deal less at this their hundredth repetition. [Even though he had enjoyed his brief visit to the school with the Major, he still bore a resentment against it:] I have not that gratitude and affection for that respectable seminary near Smithfield — which I am told good scholars always have for the place of their education; I cannot think that school to be a good one, when as a child, I was lulled into indolence & when I grew older & could think for myself, was abused into sulkiness and bullied into despair.

He found that he was clenching his pen with the intensity of his feeling, and changed the subject abruptly. This philippic must seem an ungrateful theme to his parents. But the wound was deep; it would be long ere it healed completely.

15

A Wine Party, and a Poem

Since he had been to a good many parties, William felt it was time to pay off the score.

He would invite about thirty guests. His rooms looked nearly as sumptuous as the Vice-Provost's: he had had them redecorated, with built-in bookcase and cupboard, and had ordered new draw curtains hung on brass rods at the windows. He wanted to show off this elegance to all his friends and acquaintances. He would ask the Charterhouse cronies — Carne, Fawsett, Mazzinghi, Young, Moody, Baker, Brome — but he would also include Badger, Hailstone, Heyworth, Wells and Hine, and a host of others he had come to know at college. He went to the caterer's to arrange for the necessary delicacies he must serve: ices and little cakes, pineapples and almond paste, customary sweetmeats that accompanied these feasts.

When the evening arrived, he was busy with preparations long before his guests put in their appearance. He pulled out the leaves of his table, and borrowed another from the man across the way. He borrowed chairs from everyone in the building. He polished his glasses and those he had borrowed from Carne. He mixed a huge bowlful of milk punch, which he set in the center of the table. (The punch, composed of milk, sack, sugar, and a plentiful sprinkling of nutmeg, was used to augment the wine so the revellers would not do away with the host's whole supply. William had received sage advice from Carne on this point: "Don't throw away all the sauterne your mother sent you on parties. It's much too good for them.") Around this he placed a ring of copper mugs, and to either side, dishes of sweet-meats. The caterer's boys would bring the other refreshments when the party was ready to commence. He took down two boxes of "segars" from the cupboard, putting one on either end of the table, and finished setting the plates and spoons around.

Soon the oaken portal resounded with the rappings of William's guests. They came in twos and threes, not often singly, and in a surprisingly short time the room was packed with men representing nearly every college in Cambridge. It was his first big party, and William felt warm and flushed with pride. You heard such exclamations as: "Segars, that's something like!" "There sits the wassail bowl — we'll sing a song ere long!" "I say, Thack, what a swell you are with these rooms!" "Milk punch; pass the cups!" Or such bits of conversation and greeting as, "Well, Carne! You've been walking in Derbyshire, I hear. When did you get back?" "I'm going to Newmarket myself next week. I shall pick up a horse and a bit of leather if I can." " 'Bit of leather!' He means *saddle*, why don't he say it?" "I'll sell you my Gibbon for five pounds; I paid eight for it. I won't need it after the history exam." "Hello, Badger! How did Thack manage to get your nose out of a book?"

Busy shaking hands with one or another, William finally lifted his voice above the babble. "Be seated, gentlemen!" He was growing anxious about the refreshments, when the caterer's boys arrived carrying a large straw hamper between them.

The pineapples and ices were done away with in short order, and the men settled down to the delights of the punch bowl while puffing on long segars. How sparkling the sauterne was, how potent the milk punch!

"An excellent party, my dear Thackeray," said Walter

Fawsett, seated next to William. "Let me pledge your continued eupepsia."

"Walter, please, there are no Dons here tonight," William chided him good-naturedly. " 'Eupepsia!' That's worse than 'salubrity!' I seem to recall a simple word, *health.* Have you heard it? — Lord, Walter, your vocabulary is enough to give one dyspepsia!"

His friend tried to pass the jibe off with a laugh, but acknowledged: "I did forget there were only gownsmen present."

William chuckled to himself. Walter would probably always be impressed with masters. The host saw to it that everyone's glass was full, and that the milk punch was being consumed as well as the wine. The guests were all lavish in praise of his party. The room was growing blue with smoke, stories were passed around the table and ballads sung. Men toasted their schools, their friends, their host. In response to this, William stood up and trolled "Old King Cole" in such a remarkably droll manner they doubled up with laughing at him. The gaiety seethed and bubbled, increasing as the evening went on. Fawsett, at the height of it, swung one arm wide and brought it down on William's back. "Dam' fine party, Thackeray!" he cried. And the others wondered momentarily what that great yell of a laugh from old Thack meant.

When the punchbowl was finally emptied, and the host opened no more bottles, when the sweetmeats were gone and the "segars" all smoked, William's guests said good night, with many fine speeches, and went rollicking down the stairs, making a great deal of noise in trying to be quiet. William, quite exhausted, rolled into bed and fell into a deep sleep at once.

He awoke the next morning with a splitting headache.

When he went into the next room, the frightful spectacle of the table swam in front of him — the remains of pineapples, melted ices with "segar" ashes in them, turned-over glasses, empty bottles, while over all hung the stale smell of tobacco from at least a million cigar butts. He put his fists up to his aching temples and turned away.

A moment later his gyp arrived, and immediately set about stirring up a glass of soda water. "This will fix you hup, sir. Nothin' like soda."

"I hope so . . . oh, my head!" groaned William, taking the glass.

A knock sounded on the door just then and he called out rather peevishly "Come," wondering which of his guests could be out at such an early hour after the party. But it was not one of his guests. It was his cousin, the august Provost of King's, come to call upon him. "I thought to find you deep in Algebra," he said coldly, as he surveyed the room.

William, slinking down in his chair, wished ardently that such amiable pastimes as wine parties had never been inaugurated.

Late in April the winner of the medal for the prize poem on the subject of Timbuctoo was announced: Alfred Tennyson carried off the honors without a rival. William, who had entered a manuscript, knew his was poor, and proceeded to rewrite it in the form of a parody. This he submitted to a Cambridge publication, "The Snob," which had sprung up a few weeks before. (Students called the townsmen "snobs" to distinguish them from gownsmen. By giving the name to their magazine, they hoped to deceive the reader into believing it was not written on the campus, so they would be able to lampoon the university as much as they pleased. To William's surprise, his "Timbuctoo" was printed in the April 30 issue, and was hailed with delight by all its readers.

Though he had not signed his name to the contribution, William was keenly excited by the comments he heard, his chest swelling within him. He could not help boasting in his letter home: " 'Timbuctoo' received much laud." But he added with honesty: "I could not help finding out that I was very fond of this same praise. The men knew not the Author, but praised the poem, how eagerly did I suck it in! 'All is vanity!' "

The young man who was to become famous for a novel called "Vanity Fair" was already aware of this universal weakness of human nature.

16

A Fateful Incident

AFTER THE JUNE EXAMS, which lasted eight hours each day for a week, and were relieved only by glorious suppers in Hall at nine o'clock (one night there was lobster, another oysters), William was worn out with study. Having had his mind on a continual stretch, he wished to let it relax.

He went down to Larkbeare laden with purchases: some flesh-colored writing paper for Mary Graham, a pair of gloves for his mother, a book for the Major, and a great many books for himself.

But somehow he did not find the atmosphere at home very restful. His mother, though happy to see him, showering him with every attention as she always did, thought it necessary to lecture him on the extravagances he had acquired at Cambridge. It was not necessary to buy so many books, or at any rate, not such costly editions. And those parties! They were really terrible. Not to mention the unspeakable habit of smoking cigars, which was more disgusting. If he wished to smoke, he must do so in the barn, or in the porter's lodge with John Goldsworthy.

Her words were soft-spoken, and accompanied by such sad reproach in her lovely eyes that William felt uncomfortable, apologetic, but he could see no need to apologize for his actions. His mother must realize that he was becoming a man. He could direct his own affairs. His money was his own — or would be in a couple of years, when he came into his patrimony. He stood looking down at her the night she finished her reproof, his tall, lanky figure leaning against the mantelpiece, one elbow crooked on the shelf, one leg carelessly crossed over the other. His grey eyes squinted at her with affected merriment through his gold-rimmed glasses, trying to laugh off his own annoyance as well as his mother's. "Come, mother, my actions have not been so dreadful as you would make them; I am in no danger of descending to Lucifer's domain! Isn't that right, sir?" He appealed to the Major.

But his stepfather, standing behind his mother's chair, merely shrugged his shoulders, at the same time throwing William a glance which plainly said, "Women are women, my boy. You must expect them to worry over you if you will insist upon bragging about your university liberties and customs."

And Polly, on a velvet hassock at his mother's feet, only reflected silently the lady's disapproval in her small, pale face. She worshipped Mrs. Carmichael-Smyth. If her aunt saw fit to condemn William on these counts, she condemned him as well.

He could see plainly that Larkbeare was not the place for him this summer. He arranged to go abroad with a Mr. Williams, a young tutor who conducted Cambridge students to the continent during the long vacation.

It was a regulation sojourn. They stayed at the "pension" of Madame La Baronne de Vaud, in the Rue Le Grand, which, in spite of its keeper's French title, was scarcely more than an English boarding house in Paris, all the pensioners being the sort who take their country with them when they travel.

The trip included conventional visits to the Louvre, Notre Dame, Versailles and the rest. They went to the Opera, and to the ballet, where they saw the famous dancer,

Taglioni, "who hath a superb pair of pins, and makes the most superb use of them," William wrote home.

In general, the journey differed little from the usual Paris residence so many Cambridge students took up during the summer. They moved to private lodgings because William was not learning as much French as he wished at the pension, yet the change added little color to his introduction to the world's gayest city. Unfortunately his escort was a staid young gentleman, lacking in imagination and spirit.

One night, however, he was ill, and William, with three other Trinity men they had run into at Tivoli Gardens, went into the boulevards unchaperoned. They found their way to the Rue de Richelieu, famous for its gaming houses, and stopped before the entrance of the most famous, Frascati's. Frascati's, where fortunes were won and lost in a night; Frascati's, where dukes, duchesses, earls, and Indian potentates met with card sharks and blackguards at the gaming tables, brought together by the strange lure of a game of chance.

The four young men stood gazing at the portals of the house for some time, while cabs or crested broughams drove up, and gentlemen in opera capes, carrying hats beautifully lined in white satin, were admitted by a footman in livery. When the doors were opened, the boys caught a glimpse of blazing chandeliers and brilliantly dressed crowds.

"Let's go in." A student by the name of Sedgewick spoke first.

As if it were a signal, they all started up the steps. William felt slight misgivings at actually going through the doors of a gambling house, but his intense curiosity overcame them at once. The air he breathed was spiced with new experience.

Inside, the largest groups were gathered for roulette, and for the game of rouge et noir. The four watched this game with particular interest. William found it fascinating; he did not care for the others nearly as much. His hand in his trouser pocket kept turning over the single sovereign he had brought along. At last he pulled it out and edged his way up to the table.

"I'm going to play," he hissed to his companions. He bought some chips. He won. His companions cheered. He played on and kept winning; he could feel the blood rushing to his head, as if he had been drinking champagne. What suspense there was to gambling! What a strange, sheer thrill to winning! He kept on and on. At one point he could have come away the winner of two hundred francs.

"Good place to stop, old boy," one of his friends advised.

"Stop? *Now?*" William laughed in his face. No, no, he was too elated, enjoying it all too much. He started to lose, but the power of chance was too strong; he kept on; lost, won, and lost again until his winnings were gone, but he broke even. His friends dragged him away to supper lest he should lose his original sovereign.

What an evening! His brain was on fire, he could not sleep all night, and when towards morning he did doze off, it was to dream of rouge et noir, rouge et noir. He was feverish over the game. He thought of nothing else for several days. Partly to get it out of his system, he wrote to his mother of the whole adventure.

"I could not tear myself away until I had lost my last piece," he admitted frankly. He had not returned to Frascati's, nor did he wish to do so. "I hope I shall never be thrown in the way of the thing again, for I fear I could not resist."

But when the post brought the next mail from England, he regretted his frankness with his mother. Mrs. Carmichael-Smyth was shocked to learn of her son's adventure and wrote a terrible letter to him immediately.

He was angry, hurt, and disappointed because his mother did not appreciate his honesty. He protested that he had learned a valuable lesson by going to Frascati's. "May God grant that you never again call me avaricious and mean when I am but curious," he wrote in return, "that you never again think because I before was ignorant, that therefore I was good; or that because I am now aware of my own weakness, I must be wicked."

His mother had been so panicky, unreasoning, and violent in her denunciation! He saw that he could no longer confide in her completely. After all, that evening at Frascati's was only a night's entertainment; dangerous perhaps, but he had sensed the danger and avoided it. Yet when he remembered the game of rouge et noir, he became excited, and queer chills ran up and down his spine.

17

The Circle Widens

THE SECOND COLLEGE YEAR began, with its reading periods
and round of parties. On a particularly fine day in November, William, walking home from the fields beyond Cambridge with a great tin box of oil colors under his arm,
decided to make a call on Mr. Williams, whom he had not
seen since they parted at the end of the long vacation. The
masterpieces he had seen in the Louvre rekindled the urge
to paint, and he had been sketching all day.

As he entered the tutor's drawing room, stooping a little
to avoid the door frame, he found himself being measured
by a pair of intelligent, amused, yet rather cynical eyes,
deeply set and dark in a white face, the chin of which
receded ever so slightly, the whole surmounted by a slab of
black hair flat across one side of his high forehead. The young
man who possessed these remarkable eyes and head was
dressed with equally remarkable conservatism, not a stickpin, not a watch chain, nor any piece of jewelry on him; not
a bit of color to his waistcoat, nor any of the frivolities of
Cambridge to be noted in his dress. He wore exceptionally
fine tweeds, a plain black tie, but no kerchief or frill. He
was tall, but rather slight in person, with delicate hands and
feet. Yet William felt that here was the most interesting,
colorful person he had seen at Cambridge so far.

"This is my friend, Edward Fitzgerald," Mr. Williams introduced them. "Ned, William Thackeray, whom I accompanied this summer."

The young man came forward and held out his hand,

still appraising the newcomer. William himself was no ordinary figure, with his great height, his full, ruddy face and large head. He was wearing a light blue embroidered waistcoat with gloves to match it, the latest Cambridge fashion. And he had a monocle fixed in his left eye, like the boulevard strollers in Paris. (He enjoyed the "air" a monocle gave a man; he would wear his spectacles for study only after this.)

"So you are Thackeray," Fitzgerald said at last. "Mr. Williams has spoken about you. Tell me, did you write that parody of "Timbuctoo" in "The Snob" last spring?"

"Of course not!" But the gleam of mischief behind William's eyeglass gave him away. "How did you guess?"

"You look as if you might be capable of it. We all enjoyed your satire, but my friend Tennyson did not deserve such treatment. His work has the touch of a true poet, I think."

"I agree with you, but I couldn't resist poking fun at the topic. Do you know Tennyson well?"

"Rather. Don't you?"

"He has sat next me in Hall a few times, but we've barely spoken beyond asking each other for the beef. I understand his brothers have had a volume of verse published already."

"That's right, but I believe that Alfred will surpass them both, once he develops his style, and deepens his philosophy."

They fell to discussing poets and poetry, forgetful of Mr. Williams, who rarely had very much to contribute. They progressed to prose, the novelists of their day as compared with those of an earlier time. William had recently begun to read "Joseph Andrews" and "Tom Jones." Indeed, he devoured all the novels of Fielding he could lay his hands on. Fielding, the father of English fiction — honest, natural, fearless, unafraid to show the underside of society, deriding the dainty manners of his contemporary, Richardson. What pitiless jibes and jeers the mock-heroic adventures of Fielding's main characters hurled at a novel like "Pamela."

"There's a writer for you!" William finished with a flourish of his big hand. "If I were ever to pursue a literary path, I should follow in his magnificent footsteps!"

"What is to stop you?" Fitzgerald asked.

"I have only a grain or two of talent. Besides, I am more interested in this." William touched his box of colors. "More than another Fielding, I should like to become another Hogarth. Actually, I suppose I shall do little besides mess up my fingers with paint." He laughed. "It's well my father left me an ample patrimony, else I should starve."

"I see we swim in the same stream of dilettantes — sorry fish, forsooth!" Edward shook his head.

Neither of them was much distressed with this state of affairs, and as they talked on, William had the impression that Edward Fitzgerald was not so much a dilettante as a discriminating scholar who studied for sheer pleasure in knowledge itself, rather than any gain to which it might be put. Before they knew it, the dinner hour had come, and taking leave of their host, they walked down to Hall together, still talking eagerly, gesticulating, laughing, arguing.

They could not sit together, though, since Edward was a senior. In Hall men were placed according to their classes. He introduced William to Alfred Tennyson, W. H. Thompson, and some of the men who, according to the alphabetical arrangement, sat near him.

From that day until the end of the term, scarcely a day passed that William and Edward did not meet. They breakfasted together; they dined at each other's rooms when they did not eat in Hall; they smoked and talked long hours in the evening. Occasionally they studied together, but then

First Term

neither did much work. The difference in temperament did not seem to hinder their friendship in the least. Edward was quiet and in many ways restrained, but he was never dull. His flow of speech was admirable, and his wit could be acid or kindly as he chose. He did not make a show of wisdom, like Carne; he was wise. He could be gay, but not flighty. He was the son of an Irish nobleman, and though he personified simplicity, he was also representative of the landed gentry in his lack of concern over worldly cares, his disdain of worldly society. He chose his friends as he pleased, without regard for their social rank. At his rooms you were likely

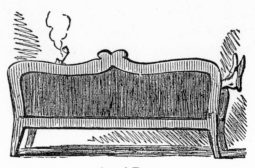

Second Term

to meet sizars and pensioners as well as noblemen and fellow commoners.

Through him William widened his circle of friends until his Charterhouse cronies became only one small group among his associates. Men like Monckton Milnes, a clever and charming young baronet, who would later assume his title of Lord Houghton; Charles and Arthur Buller (whose parents proved to be friends of the Thackerays in India), handsome, genial brothers from an upper middle class family; William Brookfield, one of the famous dandies of Cambridge, good-looking, brilliant, an admirable mimic, with whom it was considered an honor to be seen; and John Kemble, called "Jackie," son of the Charles Kembles, first family of the English stage, whose company was continual entertainment. All of these and more met in Edward Fitzgerald's rooms.

Although "Fitz" was William's closest intimate, John Kemble and "Willy" Brookfield were his fast friends before long. The four often formed a group for the theater and supper, standing in the stalls at all the performances of strolling theatrical players that stopped in Cambridge.

"Shall you tread the boards when you've earned your degree, Jackie?" William asked him one night as they sat consuming an oyster stew in Fitz's rooms, hard upon "As You Like It."

"I haven't decided yet," was the answer. "My father has received great renown, but I have seen the hardship under the grease paint and tinsel, the darkness that often follows the glare of footlights. I may choose to work upon the literature of the theater as my career. What does it matter? 'All the world's a stage, and all the men and women merely' . . ." he began to quote.

"We know you can surpass the foul Jacques we just heard,

Kemble," Fitzgerald spoke up. "You needn't play a part with us."

John blushed, but had the grace to laugh. "You see, once the theater takes hold, you never get away from it! We're all blessed — or cursed — with the desire to act. My sister Fanny makes her debut at Covent Garden next week as Juliet, may God help her."

"Oh, but we must all go to Town for her debut!" William forgot his bowl of stew. "I for one shan't miss it."

"Nor I," seconded Willy and Fitz.

The four travelled down to London for the great event. They bought seats in the pit for the occasion, filled with a sense of importance at having the brother of the star among their number. John was nervous and tense; the others had to calm his fears time after time before the curtains actually parted.

After Juliet's opening speech, however, they all knew his fears had been idle. What a superb performance, what wild acclaim Fanny Kemble received from the audience and critics! She was young, beautiful, and possessed of a voice like music. Afterwards, they must all go back to the star's dressing-room, where the admirers were waiting with flowers and invitations to supper, young noblemen in evening clothes, London rakes and men of fashion begging favors from the newest and brightest star the theater had seen in many a season.

But she accepted none of these. She went instead on a little supper-party her father and mother gave, a family party which included the three Cambridge cronies of brother John. They toasted Fanny Kemble with champagne, and sang her praises, while she blushed prettily and her eye sparkled more than the wine. Her father proudly and merrily told them how he had coached his daughter, now and again quoting from Shakespeare in his rich, baritone voice. What a fascinating family they were! William had never met such people. He determined to know them better.

"I sometimes come to London for the short vacations," he whispered to Fanny under cover of the general hubbub. "I . . . know you will be busy, but might I come to call?" He was amazed at his own boldness.

But Fanny gave him a radiant, friendly smile, and said of course Mr. Thackeray might come. They would always be glad to see him. This was not exactly what he meant, but he was happy to be accepted as a friend of the family. And separately, secretly, Willy Brookfield made a similar arrangement, while even old Fitz, who paid little attention to ladies, cast admiring glances on fair Fanny Kemble all the evening.

They were all three half in love with her by the time they went back to Cambridge. Before a week was up, all three had a copy of her portrait by Lawrence hanging in their rooms. William and Edward were in the habit of taking long walks before class, and they would talk of Fanny Kemble, her voice, her eyes, her figure, her soft brown curls, the way she had spoken the line, "Wherefore art thou Romeo," while they paced the streets and fields of Cambridge, aflame with the fever of the footlights.

"Why don't you write verses to the lady?" Edward suggested on one of these walks. "You know a new magazine is going to be published soon. The "Gownsman," I think it is to be called."

"If I compose verses, so must you, Ned," William told him; "at least you must help me. You are more of a poet than I."

"Nonsense, all I have is a talent for dullness! No, it will be a long time before I write, Thack, but you have a facility in expressing yourself. If you choose, you can do so through your sketches as well."

"Now you are calling me a dilettante again."

"Not necessarily. But since your pen is so ready, I think you should contribute to the 'Gownsman.'"

"Very well, you have convinced me," William grinned. "You see how difficult it was!"

And he did contribute, not only verses, which he labeled, "To Genevieve," but articles, and pictorial puns, which won him no small fame. A drawing entitled, "Taking in toe," might show a man booting another in the seat of the pants. "Full length" showed a lanky, lazy fellow, stretched out on the floor. He also drew all sorts of horseback riding cartoons,

men falling from their mounts, or being thrown; horses, "just a little playful"; men, "well on" and "ill off." Many of these described his own experiences. He had been renting a horse at the Cambridge stables this year, since most of the students rode and he did not want to be left out. Rates were high, but he felt he could run up an account. He would have plenty of money for all bills when his patrimony came in.

He enjoyed Edward Fitzgerald's vital conversation and company more than that of anyone he had met in all his years of schooling. He became more and more used to the ways of Fitz and his circle. He gave many little dinners for four or five men, and supper parties for more.

He was lost for days when "old Fitz" took his degree in February, 1830, and left Cambridge for a long sojourn in France.

18

Stolen Journey

"WHERE ARE YOU GOING, Thackeray?" the Proctor asked pleasantly.

"To Huntingdonshire," William answered easily, "with my friend Slingsby, sir."

"I see. Just be sure that you are back in time for Lecture next Wednesday."

"Yes, sir. I shall be back in time." William left the Proctor's office quickly.

He was not going to Huntingdonshire, and he had never heard of "Slingsby." He was going to Paris, and his friend was Edward Fitzgerald. It had to be a surreptitious visit, because gownsmen were not allowed to go out of the country without leave, and to get leave one must have an excellent excuse, or put in for permission in advance, and William could fulfill neither of these stipulations. He had a few days following exams at Eastertime, and he had got hold of twenty pounds, never mind how. Fitz had suggested that he spend those few days and pounds in Paris, and with no more notice than this, William made hasty preparations and set out for the gay city.

Fitz met him at Calais, and though it had been no more than two months since they had seen one another at Cambridge, they hailed each other with wild enthusiasm, shouting an effusion of nicknames as William came down the gangplank.

"Hall-oo, Ned! My dear old Fitz! Teddibus, mon ami!"

"Welcome, Bill! My dear old Thack! Willy, you wag,

how did you manage it?" They shook hands vehemently,
and thumped shoulders, and looked each other up and
down.

"I am not here, you understand," William warned his
friend. "I am in Huntingdonshire, with Slingsby."

"Slingsby? Oh, come now, Thack. You might have made
a more plausible choice. The Proctor must have known!"

"I give you my word he didn't suspect me in the least.
Matter of fact, he was so pleasant I fear I shall feel guilty."

"Nonsense, I shan't give you a chance. This time you will
really see Paris. Hello, here's our coach."

Once arrived at the French metropolis, Edward and
William set about taking in the pleasures of the great city
with a will. Paris in the spring was an enchantress, beckon-
ing them forth from an early hour each morning until the
gas lamps were winking out along the boulevards late at
night. The horse chestnut trees formed an overhead arch-
way of delicate green down the Champs-Elysées. The dome
of Notre Dame was a misty grey against the fresh, moist blue

of an April sky, looking down with protective peacefulness upon the brightly dressed throngs in the streets. Some sat at the sidewalk cafés sipping eau sucré, or perhaps a stronger drink. Some shopped at the famous fashion salons. Some promenaded on foot or in a carriage up and down the boulevards. But everybody, no matter what his business in Paris, whether native or tourist, seemed to be on a perpetual holiday.

Paris in the spring was a festival, at which the two young men from Cambridge were among the merriest revellers.

They went to dine at little, out-of-the-way places, cafés that Mr. Williams had probably never dreamed existed, where you could order nothing but French food, where they made no attempt to duplicate the everlasting roast beef and mutton most Britons demanded, Paris or no. Fitzgerald knew them all, these little truly-Parisian cafés, and it was at one of them, Terre's Tavern, in Rue Neuve des Petits Champs, that William was introduced to bouillabaise.

It was with some hesitation that he stuck his spoon into that delightful dish of sea-foods and sherry, of green herbs and seasonings and who knows what else? One taste of the succulent, enchanting mixture sent him into raptures.

"*C'est une poème!*" he cried out to Fitz. "But really a poem. And what a wonderful name: *bouillabaise!*" He tasted it again. "I could write a ballad on such a dish, hanged if I couldn't."

"I think it warrants at least a ballad, if not a sonnet," said Fitzgerald. "Bouillabaise is one of the treats of France."

With Edward, William tramped sections of the city he had not seen with his staid tutor. The Left Bank, the busy, noisy, sprawling, smelly side of the Seine; Montmartre, the Latin Quarter, where dwelt the artists of Paris in easy, bohemian poverty. Their wares, displayed along the sidewalk, tempted William into parting with a small portion of his twenty pounds. The rest was spent at theaters, the opera, the races, and once — only once — they went to Frascati's.

"I shouldn't, you know," William admitted to Fitz; "gambling sets me on fire. I seem to lose my head."

"Come away, then." Fitz took his arm. "We've plenty else to do."

"No, I want to prove how strong I am. I shall just observe," William insisted. But he did not remain an observer for long: five of his twenty pounds was lost at the gaming table. What was it, what was it, that caught hold of a man and made him want to gamble?

The two friends talked it over as they smoked and philosophized in youthful fashion.

"If I were you, I should not try my luck, that's all," Fitzgerald advised him. "Not that money is important, but it is one of the meaner necessities man has created. If it pains you to lose, then desist."

"Very simple! It's not the money, but the desire that bothers me. I can't forget it, hang it all, Fitz, I can't."

But after a day spent at Versailles, in the poetic atmosphere of Fitzgerald's discourse on the history of France, William did forget, and the remainder of this whirlwind, secret visit was an unbroken delight. Only when he left the fair city of lights for Calais once more, hardly enough in his pocket to pay his fare and a meager dinner when he reached England, did he suffer guilt — guilt at having gone without leave, at having spent nearly twenty pounds in a few days, at having given in, even briefly, to the strange lure of gambling. The return trip was a misery, but back at Cambridge, undiscovered — what a lark, what a spree, that week in Paris with "old Fitz"!

19

Écarté: A Grim Lesson

THE CRISES in our lives usually commence in a very small way, building up so gradually, so imperceptibly that catastrophe seizes us unawares. When William went to Frascati's the first time, it had been merely a jaunt. If his mother had not carried on so, he might have dismissed the evening from his mind entirely, though certainly he had been intrigued by the play.

But what harm could it do to join a game of cards now and then? He could see none, and if the truth be known, the twenty pounds he had just squandered in Paris had been won at a few friendly gambling sessions with some of his classmates. His second trip to Frascati's, with Fitzgerald, had shown him that the fascination of the gaming tables was as strong as ever, but he thought if he kept away from professional houses he would be safe.

During the last term of the year, a good many dinners were given by the Cambridge circle in which William moved. He himself gave a good many. More than once the caterer's boys ran up and down his steps of an evening. More than once the caterer's duns knocked at his door, requesting that a little something be paid on Mr. Thackeray's bill, which was mounting higher and higher. It was customary for college men to run up accounts. William preferred to follow the custom of the others rather than pay his bills as he went along. When his patrimony came, he would take care of everyone at once. Another year and he would come into his inheritance. By then he hoped to be an

optime, or honor man. There were wranglers, the highest
senior honor men, and junior and senior optimes. He could
not hope to be in the highest class, but he would be satisfied
to be an optime. An honor man, with money of his own,
would command no little respect from his fellows at Cambridge.

A University Tradesman

His time was so taken up with social activities, however —
not to mention outside interests like writing for "The
Gownsman," of which he became co-editor — that he neglected his reading, and in the May exam was put in the
fourth class.

He was not too much upset by this classification. If he
did not gain any honors at Cambridge, he was acquiring the
"tone" of a university man, and what was most important,

he was thoroughly enjoying the pleasant, easy life of a university man.

He missed Edward this term, but he was becoming more acquainted with some others in the new circle. He and Tennyson had met a few times, and discussed poetry. He saw John Kemble nearly as often as he had Fitz, and John Allen stopped by almost every day. He went walking arm in arm with Willy Brookfield, and felt like a celebrity, because Brookfield was an outstanding Cambridge figure. He rode with the Buller brothers, and was never omitted from their dinners.

To one of these, around the first of June, he arrived rather late. The guests were already seated, the sole was being served. Arthur Buller, whose handsomeness was so exceptional that he had already gained a reputation for it, to his embarrassment, placed William at his end of the table.

"I want you nearby to defend my point of view," he said under his breath. "We have been discussing the reform bills Parliament must provide soon. Tell me, why are the liberals always in the minority?"

"Because, my dear Arthur, it takes courage to be a liberal," William shrugged, seating himself next to his host. "And how many of us have courage? Ah, sole! I'm famished." He picked up a fork and fell to with his usual hearty appetite.

Arthur laughed, and introduced him to his neighbors, two gentlemen he had never met before. They were not gownsmen, and appeared to be somewhat older than the students. Both had the look of men of the world, polished, distinguished. They even faintly reminded William of the rakes he had seen at Frascati's. Perhaps it was the diamond stickpin glittering on the stock of the older man, Dexter, or the way the younger, Kean, moved his fingers languidly when he spoke, with splendid boredom.

When he could safely do so, under cover of the general conversation, William murmured to Arthur, "Who are they?"

"I don't know. Savile Morton brought them," was the reply.

"Ah." If the gentlemen were friends of Savile Morton, they must be men of the world. Morton was brilliant, reckless, suave, unstable in money matters, but possessed of infinitely good taste in the fine arts. You could hear him at the next table, speaking in a rapid, slightly nervous manner, gesticulating with those extremely white hands of his, while his tablemates listened with a kind of fascination. If Morton had brought these men, they bore the mark of distinction in that fact alone.

The meal advanced from fish to joints of mutton; to fowl and side dishes; to dessert. William ate, drank, and discussed politics on the side of his host. At the height of his enthusiasm for the Whig cause, he lifted his glass of claret to Arthur. "I promise you, Buller, when I receive my patrimony I shall buy a newspaper, and we shall print only articles which will further the liberal cause!"

"Huzzah!" shouted Arthur, drinking his claret to the accompaniment of boos from the conservative students.

"A commendable scheme, Mr. Thackeray," Dexter spoke up, offering his hand to William. "I only hope your patrimony is large enough to allow the purchase of a newspaper," he added kindly.

"I daresay it is not what most men would consider large," William said modestly, "but I think I can easily afford the price of some half-defunct periodical, into which I could breathe a little life."

"I see. I think the possibilities are excellent." Dexter smoothed his well-oiled whiskers thoughtfully.

Coffee and cigars were passed around, and then, as usual,

the men broke into groups, some to talk over their wine, some to play cards. As dearly as William loved talk, listening to it, and sometimes participating in it, he loved a game of cards more just at this time when he was learning the fine points. He fancied himself rather an expert, compared to some of the students who seemed to have no "card sense" at all. He sat down at one of the tables and took a hand at écarté with John Kemble.

Écarté was a fast-moving game played between two people, which had become popular in England since it had been brought over from France a few seasons before. Another year and it would give way to another game, but at present it was all the rage.

William played intently, as he always did, a frown on his forehead, releasing his eyeglass from time to time, and fixing it again before it had a chance to drop and swing on its black cord. He won, lost, won; two out of three games; not bad, not bad.

"Not bad, Thackeray." It was Dexter's voice, like an echo of his thought. "If you had been a bit sharper, you'd have won all three." He offered to give William a few pointers.

Neither of the two strange gentlemen had played, but stood behind the students, smoking and looking on. Dexter now sat down and explained the subtleties of the game, showing just how William could have won the second.

"Never mind teaching him more than he knows already," John grumbled. "Thackeray wins too often as it is!"

"Only because I'm quicker than you, Jackie, my boy." William pretended to mock his skill, but he could not keep the quiver of elation out of his words. "Tell me more, Dexter!"

And that gentleman obliged by explaining with experimental games until the party broke up.

Toward the end of the week, William was just leaving for Chapel when he saw Mr. Dexter coming from an apartment across the way.

"Kean and I have decided to spend a few months in your academic atmosphere." Dexter smiled blandly. "It has been a long time since I kept a term at Cambridge. I hope to audit some lectures."

"Splendid," William said warmly. "Since you are my neighbors, I trust we shall meet often. You must give me a chance to try my luck at écarté now that you have taught me the tricks!"

Dexter laughed loudly. "Very well, my impetuous young friend. Shall we set a date?"

"Any time you wish."

"Why not tomorrow evening then? Kean and I should be delighted to have you take dinner with us, and then we shall have a game."

"I should be delighted to come." William bowed, pleased that he had received such an early invitation.

He arrived promptly at the rooms across the street the next night, carefully dressed and groomed for the occasion. The suave elegance of his hosts impressed and somewhat subdued him at first, but after the excellent dinner, when they settled down to wine and écarté, he became more at ease, especially when he found himself winning steadily. He stood Dexter first, then Kean. He won from both. The gentlemen played for rather high stakes, but as long as he was ahead, why not keep on?

"Enough, enough!" Dexter protested about midnight. "Thackeray, you will break us. This is what I deserve for letting out my secrets."

"You shall have your chance for revenge, gentlemen," William promised gaily. "Thank you for a charming evening."

They arranged to take up the contest a couple of nights later, and William strolled across the street, whistling to himself, his spirits as high as Newton's tower.

At the next engagement with his newly-acquired, card-playing friends, he won again, and also at the one following, and the one after that. It seemed as if he could not lose. He boasted to his cronies about his ability, and challenged them all to try to beat him at écarté. He broke engagements with the others to closet himself across the street with Dexter and Kean. He was so taken up with the pastime that some of his cronies found cause to worry. John Allen, who was studying for the clergy, dropped in on William one day with John Kemble, and both of them protested against the time he was giving to cards.

"It's no good, Thack," Kemble said. "You can't neglect everything else for a mere game of chance."

"Not chance, Kemble, skill! I've been winning consistently, so where's the harm?"

"If you win, you rob the other man's purse. If you lose, you rob your own. Either way it is a sin, Thackeray." John Allen's face was very serious.

"Nonsense, the game is fair. If I am better than my opponents, I merit their money. If I'm worse, I deserve to lose. But I shan't lose, so stop fretting, both of you."

The two left, shaking their heads, and Allen said, as he closed the door, "I shall pray for you, Thackeray."

William was honestly moved that his friends should be so concerned for his welfare, but he was too much taken with the play to stop. Moreover, Dexter and Kean would probably not allow him to quit while he was so far ahead. Honor demanded that he give them the chance to win some of it back.

And the night came, not long afterward, when they did begin to win some of it back. Once begun, their winning

streak kept on, until William's gains were nearly gone. The
tide had turned, and just as he had won steadily, so now
he lost, and lost, and lost. His opponent Kean, his own
better judgment, both counselled him to stop when he was
even, but it was in the middle of the evening. If he kept on,
perhaps he could retrieve half of his former winnings.

He played as if possessed by fever. He dropped his
monocle but forgot to refix it, letting it swing back and forth
on the black cord until it came to rest against his waistcoat,
unheeded. He did not know how much he lost that night.
He stumbled across the street weary and red-eyed. He slept
uneasily, in a kind of daze.

In the morning, before he had a chance to rouse himself
from this state, Dexter and Kean came over to present their
bills. William had signed I.O.U.'s amounting to over
fifteen hundred pounds.

He passed his hand over his eyes, unbelieving. "I can't
have lost this much."

"Ah, but you did." Dexter's face leered above him.
"There is your signature."

"Perhaps I can win tonight . . . "

"I'm sorry. We are leaving Cambridge today," Dexter
said.

"Leaving?" William started off the sofa wildly. "But you
must give me another chance!"

"I'm sorry, we have been called to Town on urgent business." Dexter's voice was as smooth as the oil on his beard.
"Now, if you will take care of this little account . . . "

"Where would I get such a sum as that?" William demanded. "I have no money!"

"I believe we can find a way." Dexter laughed unpleas-
antly. "You have a patrimony . . . "

"Just sign it over to us, and we will call it even," Kean
added.

His patrimony! His long-awaited patrimony. Most of his father's estate, in the East Indian bank, would come due in the form of annual income. But part of it was to be paid in a lump sum, amounting to about fifteen hundred pounds. William closed his eyes, his head swimming. Suddenly he stood up, his fists clenched.

"You planned to do this," he accused the men. "Vultures! Oh, why was I so blind?"

"My dear Thackeray, don't be so melodramatic," Dexter said.

"I won't pay it!" William roared, towering over them.

"I think you will. Gentlemen usually pay debts of honor."

"Honor!" William scoffed. But he knew it was useless to protest. He put on his coat, and drove in the men's cabriolet down to the office of his broker in the city, where he signed away his patrimony to the two card sharks.

That night he did not sleep. Shame and remorse would not let him. What would he say to his mother? And she to him? He dreaded to think of it. And what would the kind-hearted Major say? His friends would be sorry for him, his enemies would laugh. Gullible Thackeray, taken in by a couple of sharpers!

He groaned with inward rage, and heard the clock strike four. One thing he knew: he was through with gambling. The lesson had been costly, but it was indelibly engraved upon his conscience. A good share of his patrimony — a patrimony was not merely an inheritance, but a particular legacy from father to son — he had thrown away lightly on a game of chance. If there were a heaven, from whose height all departed souls might regard those left on earth, what would his father's opinion be of so profligate a son?

When the dawn stole in through the windows, William was on his knees by the bedside.

20

A Comic-Opera Kingdom

ONCE HIS LOSSES were known, the duns knocked steadily on William's door. Whenever he left his rooms or came home, the caterer's dun, the livery stables' or the tailor's dun would be waiting on the landing to present his bill. Sometimes two or three of them were gathered there. News that he had sold out part of his patrimony soon escaped, try as he did to hide it, and the panicky tradespeople hurried to collect whatever might be salvaged for their accounts.

It was most embarrassing. Dismayed and disheartened, William decided to make a clean breast of his misfortune at Larkbeare, and ask his parents to take care of his most pressing bills. He was not sure he wanted to receive his degree from Cambridge. He had lost his taste for college life.

To his surprise, his mother had a great deal less to say than he had expected.

"I thought something was amiss when you wrote so seldom," she said when he finished his woeful tale. "Why didn't you tell me?"

"Because I knew you would kick up a dreadful row, and I thought a few games of écarté would do me no harm, as long as I stayed ahead. I realize now that you were right in being so alarmed about my trip to Frascati's. I resented your violence at the time, but now I understand it, mother."

"I believe you, William." Her son's eyes told her that he had suffered a great deal, that he needed no more verbal lashing than he had inflicted upon himself. "We must see,

162

first of all, that your debts are paid," she said practically. Her hands, slim and dainty beneath the huge, bell-like sleeves of her gown, went through the stack of bills William had brought with him.

He was grateful to his mother for being so matter-of-fact, but his shame was increased by her attitude, and by that of his stepfather, who, as always, expressed his understanding of William's extravagance. Mary Graham, too, was generosity itself.

She had grown quite suddenly into a lovely young girl since he had last been home, so that it was William's turn to be shy with his cousin. She was coming through the green door in the wall, her arms full of flowers from the garden, when he went into the yard for his horse the morning after his arrival.

"William," she stopped him; "wait a minute." She came up to him. "My parents didn't leave me much, you know, but I do have a small inheritance, and if you would like to borrow some of it . . . " She hesitated, in some confusion.

"Dear Mary, what a good little sister you've been! You are all too kind to me. I have my own inheritance, remember. I shall have an income of a few hundred a year." This was true, but at the moment he was without funds. "Only — could you lend me a couple of shillings for some cigars, Polly?"

His cousin burst out laughing. "Of course I can, you goose! Let me deposit these flowers, and I'll come back with your shillings."

William rode into Ottery St. Mary, bought his cigars, stopped to chat with Dr. Cornish, and rode listlessly back to Larkbeare, wondering how he should spend the summer.

It was the habit of Cambridge men to take up residence in a small principality in Europe for some months after finishing college. Since William had just about decided not to take a degree, why shouldn't he enjoy the taste of continental life immediately? The more he thought about the idea in the days that followed, the better he liked it. He recalled conversations on the subject with some of his cronies before school closed.

The little court of Weimer stood in high favor among the students who wished to learn the German language and at the same time lap up a little continental culture. James Young had promised William letters of introduction to "the best families" from his mother, who "knew everyone worth knowing in Europe." Several other Cambridge men had spoken of going to Weimar, and the end of July found William preparing to leave for Cologne by the next passage.

The boat was crowded, and as there were no beds on board, the voyagers slept wherever they could, on chairs, sofas, stools, and blankets laid on the floor. William found a coal pile on deck, which served as a place to curl his long body.

He stopped in Godesberg a few days, where the quaint dress of the students, including the stocking-caps, swords, and absurdly long pipes they carried, the duels and duelling clubs they formed, impressed him so that he sent home sketches of them. From there he continued down the Rhine to Weimar.

To William, as to most travellers in that picturesque country, the city of Weimar was like a make-believe kingdom in a comic opera, with its bustling, ceremonious court, where all the world must be in uniform: its Prince, Karl Friedrich, and silly Grand Duke Herzog, its university students, dressed for the most part like those in Godesberg, not to forget its circle of ladies and maids-in-waiting, clustered about the court like bunches of flowers in full bloom.

German student of the period. (Weimar, 1830)

William had a chance to view the showy little retinue at close range, for one of the first people he met was William Lettsom, co-editor of "The Snob," who was now attached to the suite of the English ministry at Weimar.

"I shall introduce you to the Von Spiegels, and the Von Papenheims, two of Weimar's finest families, and they will present you at Court," Lettsom promised; "but you ought to wear a uniform, Thack."

"What must I do — rent one at a costume shop? I never wore a uniform in my life!" William protested.

"Well, at least wear black; and breeches are the style here, you know," Lettsom warned him.

"Yes, yes, I shall rig up a proper outfit. It's like going to a masquerade ball."

"And even more diverting," Lettsom laughed. "I will take you calling next week. Incidentally, the two reigning beauties of Weimar happen to be the daughters of the families I mentioned."

"If I had known, I should have come prepared! But I shall be ready for you."

In the meantime, William had to become acquainted with the German master he had selected, one Frederich August Wilhelm Weissenborn, a well-known character in Weimar. Herr Weissenborn was a cultivated scholar, who combined strange eccentrics with a gentle, unselfish nature.

He met William in his study, with his two pets, whom he introduced: "My dog, Waltina, Herr Thackeray, and my little chameleon." He pointed with his thumb to the tiny creature, turned so nearly the color of the desk top on which it perched that one could scarcely see it. "He is a fruitful source of my theory on the Kosmos."

Sensing that the old master regarded his pets with the utmost seriousness, William bowed to both of them. "I am happy to make the acquaintance of Herr Weissenborn's companions."

The tutor's wrinkled face lit up with appreciation, but almost immediately sobered, and he drew his velvet-collared smoking jacket closely about him, at the same time patting his right side with tender concern. "Now, if it is agreeable to my side, we may discuss your course. What would you like to read, young man?"

William was nonplussed by the teacher's gesture and words, but he gave no sign that he thought them extraordinary, and in the weeks that followed, he was to learn that Herr Weissenborn, a confirmed invalid, always referred to "my side" as if it were an exacting member of his household. "My side wants a hot water-bottle"; or, "my side demands rest; the session is over for today," were not unusual statements from the good doctor of philosophy. Sometimes he would interrupt a translation with an account of what "my side" went through the night before.

Yet for all his eccentricities and complaints, his English students loved the doctor, and he in turn treated them like a father. William went through "Faust" with him, borrowed money from him when the weekly allowance from Larkbeare ran out, and confided in the old man when the two court beauties caused his heart to hammer.

For William fell in love at first sight when he met Melanie Von Spiegel. His schoolfellow Lettsom came to fetch him one evening as he had promised, and they set out for the home of Baron Von Spiegel, Lord Marshal of Weimar. A tailor had turned William's trousers into black breeches, and he was sporting a black coat, black waistcoat and a cock hat. "I realize that I look like a cross between a footman and a Methodist parson," he said; "but it shan't be for long. I have written to my mother asking her for an absurd favor — a cornetcy in Sir John Kennaway's yeomanry." (Kennaway was the nobleman from whom his parents rented Larkbeare.)

"Splendid; your uniform in the yeomanry will be just the thing here," Lettsom approved. "Ah, we've arrived."

The Von Spiegels were expecting them — the pompous, round little Baron, the buxom, round little Baroness, his wife, and the beautiful blond Melanie, their daughter. Melanie — it was a comic-opera name, and she looked like a comic-opera heroine: all pink and white and smiling, blond curls on her shoulders, and eyes like twin blue stars. William was completely bowled over by her smiles, her gestures, her interest in "Herr Thackeray." Luckily (and this was true of all the daughters of Weimar) she could speak English, but her mamma could not, and William paid Miss Melanie many extravagant compliments as they sat on the sofa together after dinner, while her mother thought he was uttering commonplaces of conversation.

The Von Spiegels were happy to present him at Court, where he was announced with great solemnity by the guard, following which he knelt, and kissed the hand of Karl Friedrich.

Then came a court ball, and dancing with Melanie. Melanie, so beautiful, soft and appealing. The musicians played a waltz, at which William was overwhelmed; he had never waltzed before, he had never before held a young girl in his arms. His head towered above his partner's, his ungainly legs moved awkwardly, certainly not in three-quarter time.

"I fear I am no dancer," he sighed, as Melanie drew her small foot quickly out of the way of his great one.

She did not deny this. "Perhaps Herr Thackeray needs a few lessons," she suggested demurely. "I know of a master."

He went to this master in the art of waltzing and gallopading and tried with all his energy to become a complete courtier. On nights when there was no ball, he wrote verses to Melanie, or went to the theater, where the Von Spiegels had a box. The boxes were laid out in gallery fashion, with no partitions between them, so you could walk from one to the other and choose your company. During intermission William nearly always managed to occupy a place by Melanie's side. He treasured in his desk drawer a blue kid glove she had accidentally dropped. He attended the dancing class regularly.

In spite of all his lessons, however, his waltzing did not improve, and one night the polished marble of the palace floor
was too much for him. He slipped and fell at Melanie's feet,
and with him fell his favor. Melanie was a maid of honor at
the court; she was not interested in a dancing partner too
gauche to learn.

William was desolate for a day or so, but within two weeks
he had lost his heart again, this time to Jenny Von Poppenheim.

Jenny, too, was a court maid of honor, and as dark a
beauty as Melanie was blond. She and her mother received
William graciously, as, indeed, they received all the young
Englishmen in Weimar. The British students, since they
could afford to spend months abroad acquiring a liberal education, obviously must come from well-to-do families, and
the mammas of Weimar were bent on making fine marriages
for their daughters.

William was charmed with Jenny, who had more wit than
Melanie. He danced with her (and did not fall down), and
took her to the cosy Weimar theater. The German stage was
not the art that the British made it. Here a performance was
more or less of a social gathering, with little thought given to
the play, but William loved even mediocre theater, and as
operas, too, were given in the house with the unpartitioned
boxes, he frequented the place, sometimes with Jenny, sometimes with another student or by himself.

At tea one day with the lady and her mamma, when the
two ladies began to talk of incomes, William was suddenly
possessed of an impulse to try a little experiment. He hinted,
merely hinted that he was going to have fifteen thousand
pounds a year, and the respect he received was quite wonderful.

"Do have some more of this cream, Herr Thackeray,"

Jenny's mother pressed him; "you know we get it from the country."

Jenny herself turned her dark eyes directly into William's. "What were you saying the other night about Schiller? I was trying to tell mamma, but I could not remember."

"I merely said I considered him a man whose religion and morals were unexceptionable — whereas Goethe has been by practice and profession a libertine."

"Yes — oh, you are so clever!"

"Ah, yes, you are right, Herr Goethe is such a fine gentleman," mamma said in German, having caught the poet's name, but not understanding William's words. "Have you met him yet?"

William choked on his tea, but managed:

"Not yet, but his daughter-in-law has promised me an interview."

"Frau Goethe will keep her word, and I am sure Herr Goethe will like you." His hostess beamed on him.

"Of course he will!" seconded Jenny. "Herr Thackeray is so interesting, so brilliant; a man of affairs."

The two ladies continued to make a fuss over him until William was quite remorseful at having misrepresented his fortune. Not wishing to carry the joke too far, he undeceived the ladies the very next day when he came to call. Jenny and her mother were polite, and pretended to smile, but from then on they did not show William so much respect, and treated him entirely without ceremony.

And one night when William came to the theater, another young man was seated in the box beside Jenny, a young man resplendent in a gold-threaded waistcoat and curling mustachios. The dark-eyed beauty had eyes only for the newcomer, her red lips smiled only at him. Poor Thackeray received the briefest nod.

"Who is the gentleman, pray?" William muttered to Lettsom, with whom he had come. "You know everyone in Weimar."

"I can't tell you his name, but I understand he has a good many of those embroidered waistcoats," Lettsom said behind his hand. "He is heir to ten thousand a year."

"Then my cause is lost," William said ironically. "That is my reward for being honest. Come, let's have a smoke. " And with a few puffs from his cigar, he blew away his infatuation for Miss Jenny von Poppenheim.

From then on, he studied a great deal more, and thought about what he should do. He explored the field of law along with the works of Schiller and Goethe. He had long talks with Lettsom about a diplomatic career, and finally wrote to his mother, who had been prodding him to decide on some profession:

> The more I see of it, the more I am sure I could work my way into an attachéship. Most of the men are rich and idle, but if a poor man be industrious, he would have double advantage. I have been taking a little recreation in the field of law. I cannot be a clergyman or physician; I must be a lawyer. If I can only mend the expensive habits that blessed University of Cambridge has taught me! I regret the time I spent there — not the employment, but the loss of money.

William was delighted with "Faust," though the masterpiece was not so profound as he had expected. He had been taken, as he said, to Frau Goethe's famous salon, but he had not yet met the poet himself. Madame Goethe made a point of inviting Englishmen to her drawing-room, to whom she was very kind, but something of a bore, so loudly did she praise and rave over English literary figures. William noticed three Byrons, a Shelley, and Moore on her table at once!

"I do so love the English poets, Herr Thackeray." She

would clasp her hands together. She kept house for her famous father-in-law, cared for him patiently, and would willingly arrange interviews with the old man for young intellectuals like William. She had taken a particular fancy to "Herr Thackeray," and went so far as to show her father-in-law some sketches William drew for her.

Goethe, at eighty-three, was the glory of Weimar and Germany. He occasionally gave tea parties to which he invited Englishmen and especial favorites of his in the town. William hoped to be invited to one of these, but he was totally unprepared for the summons he received one morning from the Goethe household. He was to appear at twelve o'clock for an interview!

He dressed carefully, and went to Goethe's private apartments shortly before noon. He was trembling when he lifted the knocker.

The poet received him in an antechamber, "covered all around with antique casts and bas-reliefs." He was dressed in a long drab redingote, with a white neckerchief and a red

Goethe.   A sketch from the Fraser portrait

ribbon in his buttonhole. He kept his hands behind his back, but greeted William cordially. "Welcome, Herr Thackeray. My daughter has spoken well of you." His eyes were extraordinarily dark, piercing, and brilliant; his complexion very bright, clear and rosy.

William bowed to the ancient figure before him, unable to speak. Goethe began to talk in French with a marked accent, which was a relief. It made him seem more human, and William was able to enter into the conversation almost with ease. The interview lasted for half an hour, though of what was said William never could be certain. He knew only that he was having a private "sitting" with Goethe, and that this would be one of the unforgettable moments of his life.

William stayed in Weimar eight months, during which time a good deal of the "rust" he had collected in school and college was rubbed off. Up to now, he had not been in the company of women except on holidays, and court twice a week, ceremonious though it might be, served as an introduction to "polite society." He learned to dance well enough so that even Melanie did not disdain him; but theirs was never more than a court acquaintanceship, for William's first delirium with regard to the belles of Weimar did not return.

He read ravenously, grew to like Schiller's poetry better than Goethe's, and purchased not only a manuscript but the court sword of Schiller to carry home with him. He thought a great deal about the profession of law, and the more he thought, the more inclined he was to enroll in the Middle Temple Court when he returned to England.

21

The Inns (and Outs) of Court

THE TEMPLE, between Fleet Street and the Thames, rose from the river bank with dark and ancient dignity, enlivened only by Temple Gardens, which led to the water's edge. Originally the quarters of the Knights Templar, it had been leased to the students of common law in 1346, and with its two divisions, the Inner and Middle Temples, marked the beginning of the area occupied by the four Inns of Court. On the other side of Fleet Street, running to Holborn, was Lincoln's Inn, with its recreation grounds, Lincoln's Inn Fields. And on the other side of Holborn, running to Clerkenwell, was Gray's Inn, the smallest of the

four. An Inn consisted of a hall, chapel, library, a suite of rooms devoted to the benchers, or senior, governing members, and sets of chambers (or offices) for barristers and solicitors.

Into one of these, No. 1 Hare Court, William turned reluctantly on the morning of June 3, 1831. Gad, what a dreary building, he thought. Why leave a sunny June day for this? But he was determined to go through with the study of law, and with a shake of his large head, fixing his monocle securely in his left eye, he strode into the smoky, dingy backshop of William Taprell, the special pleader with whom he was going to read.

Inside, there were a number of tall, slanting, pulpit-like desks, before which students on high stools sat busily reading and jotting down notes from the great thick volumes open across their desk tops. Because of the murky light in the shop, some of the men used oil lamps, and wore visors to avoid the glare. Others crouched over their books, squinting to make out the small type.

William approached the nearest pulpit. "Can you tell me where I might find Mr. Taprell?" he asked a young fellow whose parchment-colored face was topped by a thatch of yellowish red hair, and whose eyes, bleary from constant close work, blinked owlishly at him.

"In there." The curt answer was given in a tone of annoyance at the interruption, accompanied by a nod toward a door opposite.

"Thank you." William went up and knocked, was admitted by the barrister, and given his instructions.

"You must, first of all, purchase a volume of Chitty," Mr. Taprell said. "No law student can carry on without Chitty. From time to time there will be other books you must buy, but Chitty is basic." He seemed disconcerted for a moment by his repetition, shrugged his shoulders and went on. "I shall give you instructions on how to draw Declarations, Rebuttals, Evictions and so forth. You will be appointed to a desk, and expected to be here working at it daily from twelve to five. Then, of course, you will do outside reading in your rooms, morning and evening, whenever you choose, but a certain amount of ground must be covered this term. You understand, Mr. Thackeray?"

"I think so."

"Very well." Mr. Taprell rose. "Come, we shall see to your place." He led the way back into the shop, where he assigned William the stool and frame next to that of his informant with the reddish hair. "Mr. Bleek, Mr. Thackeray," he introduced them.

Bleek had time for no more than the merest acknowledgment before he crouched once more over his study, and William, at a loss to know what to do, decided he would go to the bookstalls in search of the compulsory "Chitty."

He had taken rooms at Number 5 Essex Court, a little

street just off the square at which Fleet Street ended and The Strand commenced — The Strand, center of London's theater district. Here were The Lyceum, The Gaiety, The Adelphi. Just over the way, up Drury Lane, stood the theater of that name, and not too much farther on, was Covent Garden market and Covent Garden theater. Yes, his rooms were indeed conveniently located, and his books could be bought tomorrow. He would take a little stroll up the Strand.

He had to confess that one of the attractions of law was the proximity of the Inns of Court to the theatrical section. He sorely missed the London stage in Europe.

> How I long for the sight of a dear green curtain! [he had written to Fitz a month ago]. Oh, the delight of seeing the baize slowly ascending, the spangled shoes which first appear, then as it draws up, legs, stomachs, heads, till finally it ends in all the glories of a party of "musqueteers" drinking. . . . Yet another month and all this Paradise will be in my reach. Really, London is to me only the place where the theaters are.

Now he was here, and here they were, waiting for his patronage. He would see what was playing and choose which of them all he should attend that night. He would only look in at Covent Garden in case the Kembles should be there. After all, he had to let his friends know he was in London, and close by, too. He walked briskly in the June sunshine, sniffing the smells from the Thames, delighting in the billows of London smoke that momentarily obscured the golden light from the sky — and putting out of his mind completely the duties that lay behind him at Mr. Taprell's dusty shop. He hurried a bit faster toward Covent Gardens . . .

"Is Mr. John Kemble in the theater?"

"Yes, sir, Mr. Kemble is rehearsing. Who is calling?"

"William Makepeace Thackeray — a Cambridge friend." Not that his name meant anything to the manager, but he made it sound imposing. He chuckled inwardly as the man motioned him into the darkened hall, where on the stage the Kembles, father and son, were in the middle of a scene from "King Henry VIII."

William slipped into a seat in the pit next to a young woman and a gentleman. The lady was Fanny Kemble, who would have let out a cry of welcome, but he put a finger on his lips and nodded toward the stage. When the scene was over, he applauded, however, and Fanny called, "Jackie, see who has come to rehearsal."

John walked to the proscenium, squinting at the theater. There was but one person whose head would make such a huge silhouette. "Thackeray, old Thack!" he shouted, jumping down from the stage, and grasping his friend by the hand. "You'll stay until we're through, won't you?"

"I shouldn't, but probably I shall." William smiled.

"Fine, then we can talk. What did you think of the last speech, Mac?" John turned to Fanny's companion.

"Capital, but I'd like to see you farther upstage at the beginning. Then you can start working back down on line five, say. — I hope you don't object, sir." This was addressed to John's father, who was directing as well as acting in the piece. The young man, whom Fanny presented to William, proved to be William Macready, a most engaging sort, who was rapidly gaining a reputation for his outstanding ability in Shakespearean roles.

After rehearsal, they all took lunch in a little restaurant near the market, during which William listened eagerly to the actors talking shop. He loved the language of the theater — the most commonplace details of a production were surrounded with an aura of indefinable sorcery, like the mysteries he read at Charterhouse, whose occult charms never waned, no matter how many times over he thumbed them. Not until the Kembles (how fetching Fanny looked in her bonnet with blue velvet ribbons and great bunches of fruit!) had finished discussing the business of the second and third acts with Macready, would William consent to tell them what he was doing in London.

John was unexpectedly enthusiastic when he heard William had enrolled in the Middle Temple. "Another year and I may join you, Thack. I'm not too fond of acting, you know."

"So you have said, while I, if I had one drop of dramatic ability, would wring it dry upon the boards. What do you prefer, my friend? A seat on the bench?" William asked satirically.

"Possibly. Or I may write some articles for magazines. And I have already outlined a book on Anglo-Saxon that I hope to begin next fall."

"On Anglo-Saxon — tell me more," William commanded.

"It will be a work without which no one can understand English — which no one can understand without understanding the other Teutonic dialects."

"I'm quite certain we all understand," William said with a droll expression, and while they were laughing, he told them about Mr. Taprell and the everlasting Chitty. And so a couple of hours passed. Full rehearsal was called for two o'clock, and since Fanny was going back, it took little persuasion on the part of Macready and the rest to induce William to return with them.

Fanny Kemble had become, if anything, more ravishing than she was on the occasion of her debut the year before. Her mannerisms, the toss of her head, the graceful movements of her white arms, were celebrated now, as well as her vibrant voice and enchanting portrayals of stage heroines. Her successes had saved her father from closing the doors of Covent Garden, which had been on the verge of failure until that memorable performance of "Romeo and Juliet." The overflow of patrons had, indeed, helped to put the Drury Lane on a sounder footing as well.

As William sat beside Fanny in the darkness again, peering at her with greater admiration than he ever had, he heard Charles Kemble addressing the little groups of actors huddled in the pit with the familiar call: "On stage, everybody. First act. Places." Oh, the enthralling language of the theater!

It had grown late by the time Mr. Kemble was satisfied with his troupe, and the family of actors invited William to come home for dinner. Their aunt, the famous Mrs. Siddons, had promised to take her mutton with them, and John had received a manuscript containing a volume of verse from Alfred Tennyson, in which he thought there were "really some quite beautiful lines." He would like William's opinion. This left no opportunity to buy law texts. He had, however, all the next morning.

Bright and early the following day found him hurrying to the Adelphi theater, where Macready had invited him to sit in on a rehearsal of "The Merchant of Venice." William and the distinguished young actor had hit it off very well; it would be too bad to miss the chance of cementing the friendship and seeing Macready in action at the same time.

When twelve o'clock arrived, the stool next to Mr. Bleek's was still empty, but a few minutes later William burst into the shop, a trifle breathless, but with textbooks in tow. He had made it! By Bleek, the others already at work, and by Taprell, the newcomer was considered tardy, and he received but a cool reception. The barrister offered his instructions and necessary explanations with mild disapproval, after which he retired to his private office, leaving William to plunge in and wrestle with legal terms as best he might.

Once begun, he read assiduously for the first week, and saw to it that he was on time faithfully. He sketched himself for his parents, showing how his lanky figure looked on the high stool as he bent over his great thick volume of Chitty. "This wonderful monster is to be seen every day between 12 and 5 at Mr. Taprell's rooms in Hare Court Temple," the caption read.

Much as he wished to call on the Kembles again, or take up his acquaintance with the thoroughly enjoyable Macready, he kept himself strictly within the confines of the Inns of Court for awhile, so that he might become immersed in the atmosphere, as well as schooled in the learning. But it was a rigourous routine. "This lawyer's preparatory education is certainly one of the most cold-blooded, prejudiced pieces of invention that ever a man was slave to — I don't mean prejudice, but prejudice-making, for a fellow should properly do and think of nothing else than law," he protested to his mother in one of his letters.

Surely, he told himself, it was not wise to become onesided. When he saw Bleek's bleary eyes every morning (that gentleman was not only his neighbor at Taprell's, but had chambers above his at Essex Court!) he shuddered to think of letting himself become such a drudge. Accordingly, once he had his work under way, he attended the theater two or three nights a week, called on the Kembles, on various friends of Macready with the actor, on his relatives, the Turners at 8 Montague Place or at his Uncle Frank's. The Ritchies had left London and gone to Paris, to his regret. He missed dropping in at Southampton Row as he had always done on coming to Town, but perhaps it was just as well there were no more distractions!

In the fall, Edward Fitzgerald came to visit him. What a grand reunion there was in William's chambers! Fitz and Thack, Henry and Jackie Kemble and the Buller brothers, all sitting around in William's small living room, with his chimney-glass ornamented by dozens of gimcracks from Cambridge, blowing great clouds of smoke into the air through teeth-clenched pipes, and talking, talking, talking — it was like being back at the University.

Edward, in fact, was on his way to become a student again. He had decided to keep another term at Cambridge while trying to make up his mind concerning his calling.

"If I knew what I wanted to do!" Edward's words came out muffled as he bit down harder on his pipe. "Now you, Thack, have finally chosen the legal profession . . . "

"Yes, at the end of thirty years I shall most likely be Lord Chancellor!"

"And you, Buller," Edward took out his pipe and pointed to Charles with the stem of it, "will probably be an M.P. one of these days."

Both brothers were reading law, Arthur with the intention of practising it, and Charles with that of becoming a figure in Parliament. "You're right, Fitz — that is, if I run a successful campaign in the family seat next year," Charles admitted with a quiet smile. "What do you say, Thack? Would you like to come to Cornwall and pull with me? Get a liberal into office?"

"I should welcome the chance with all my heart," William said.

"There, you see?" Edward pointed out. "I'm not interested in law, or politics, or like the Kembles here, in the theater, except as a spectator. Alfred Tennyson, I think, will

Thackeray's Mother

"The Governor"

Larkbeare

Thackeray Sketches His Home and Parents

Thackeray as a Young Man, 1832

gain recognition as a poet. I should like to write poetry, too, but I feel I haven't the ability. I can criticize Alfred's work, tell him what is wrong, but whether I could compose verses that are as good is another matter."

"Can a man judge of his own abilities?" William asked, adjusting his monocle thoughtfully. "I was twenty the eighteenth of July. My life so far has been a melancholy succession of idleness and dissipation." He laughed ruefully, remembering the reason he left college. "And yet — don't you think that every fellow has the consciousness of having something superior within him, with the nature of which he's unacquainted, though certain either from fancy or conceit of its existence? I see people do things far better than I, and yet somehow my extreme good opinion of myself is by no means lowered."

"Conceit; you hit on it there, old boy!" Jackie Kemble twitted him, while the others laughed.

But Fitz leaned forward in his chair. "I believe Thack is merely alluding to one's self-esteem, what the French mean when they say *amour-propre*; what La Rochefoucauld refers to as a kind of greatness that comes from the value we insensibly set upon ourselves. Thack and I didn't belong, but didn't the rest of you, Tennyson and some of the others, band together and call yourselves The Apostles? Apostles, indeed! And yet no group at Cambridge won more respect."

They wrestled with the subject for some time. William had a little dinner sent up, and in the evening they went in a body to attend the fall opening at Covent Garden, where Fanny and Mr. Kemble were making a joint appearance.

Edward and William went to the pit nearly every night thereafter until it was time for Fitz to leave. They loitered in the bookstalls of mornings (after a cup of "fat chocolate" in Regent Street), read or dropped in at rehearsal in the afternoon, and took in some performance or other in the evening. Poor Mr. Taprell was forgotten for three days in a row while Fitz and Thack celebrated their reunion.

Then his guest was off to Cambridge, leaving William's chambers at Essex Court quite desolate. Luckily John and Henry Kemble dropped in for breakfast the next morning, and he passed the whole day in their lively company, so that by the following day he had recovered from his loneliness and settled down to work again.

Not that it was easy. He found himself distracted by all sorts of diversions. He went to a performance of "Beggar's Opera," which he considered "the pleasantest play in our language to see." Then the pantomimes would be coming in a few days — huzza! How he loved the lavish fantasies, fairy tales that never lost their enchantment.

Ideas for new enterprises kept popping up in his brain. During Fitzgerald's stay, he and William had translated poetry, on which Edward daily spent hours. William now sent his version of the German poem, "Feld Marschale," to James Fraser, editor of "Fraser's Magazine." With the manuscript went a timid note:

Dear Sir:
  I have ventured to send you a translation of Arud's "Feld Marschale." It may perhaps be worthy of a vacant page in your magazine. I am, dear Sir, your obdt. servt.,
                                        W. M. Thackeray

If Mr. Fraser accepted his offering, William would submit more.

As a student in the Middle Temple, he did everything but study law.

22

Venture Into the Fourth Estate

As soon as he heard the insistent staccato sounded on his door, William opened it to the smiling face of his friend Macready, whom he was expecting. It was a fine evening, and the two were going out.

"Greetings and salutations. I see you're ready," Mac bowed.

"And waiting!" William snatched up his coat and gloves. "Where shall we go tonight?"

"Does it matter? Wherever our feet take us," Macready cried.

"Agreed!"

And down the steps they went, passing poor Bleek on his way up to his rooms for an evening of solitary study. Indeed, he had no other sort, and seemed to grow paler, more blood-shot from eye-strain by the hour. He gave the two "dandies" a look of disdain and disapproval. Taprell wasn't going to catch *him* unprepared. Let Mr. Thackeray have all the good times he chose. He, Bleek, would know the law when he got through. So he insinuated to William when they stopped for a few moments' chat on the landing now and then, or when he rapped on the floor for quiet during some party in the rooms below.

"I wouldn't trade habits with him for all the legal knowledge in the world," William remarked when Bleek was safely past. "He is not really alive — merely a studying automaton, a blind grub."

Mac had the evening's activities on his mind. "I told the

Chadwicks we would stop in to see them for a bit," he began, referring to some friends with whom he had acquainted William; "but if you would rather not . . . "

"On the contrary, I'm delighted. There's usually good cheer at the Chadwicks'," William assured him.

But when they arrived, a sad little scene was taking place in the drawing-room. Mrs. Chadwick sat stern-faced before a small boy on a hassock at her feet, who was sobbing, and refused to look up when his mother spoke to him. She nodded to the visitors, and shrugged her shoulders helplessly, gesturing toward her son.

"What's the matter with Eddy?" Macready inquired.

"He is crying his eyes out because he can't learn the alphabet," Mrs. Chadwick told them. "I have been telling him to try harder, but he only sobs all the more."

"No wonder — it's such a very dull thing to learn." William bent down and pulled one of the boy's short curls, but still the child would not look up. Two of his sisters were standing by, hands behind their backs, taking in the scene. "Will you fetch me a large sheet of notepaper?" William asked one of them, struck by a sudden idea. "Maybe we can put a little life into the old alphabet."

The girl ran off to the nursery and brought him the notepaper.

"Ah, that's it, thank you." He took the paper and began to fold it carefully, over and over, while they all watched him curiously; even Eddy half lifted his head to see what was going on.

"What are you going to do?" The older of the girls could contain herself no longer.

"We're going to help Eddy with his abc's, and have a good time doing it." William sat down in the chair, which Mrs. Chadwick had quietly vacated, and, taking the stubby drawing pencil he always carried from his waistcoat pocket, began to sketch a grotesque-looking monster. Eddy got up and stood at the side of the chair to see better, while the girls grouped themselves on the other side.

When he had finished the cartoon, William printed beneath it:

> Great A; it is an animal and called an Alligator,
> Its countenance will show you that it's of a cruel Natur.

" 'Gator and natur — oh, I say, Mr. Thackeray!" The girls giggled over his ingenious rhyme, while their brother jumped about, commanding joyfully: "Now 'B'; do 'B'!"

William had already turned to the next square, and with a few strokes pencilled the picture of a bed much too short for its owner, whose bare feet stuck out at one end of it. He wrote below this:

> B is a bed and in it, a young gentleman doth lie;
> All I can say, I'd rather that he were there than I.

The children let out a shout, the loudest part of which came from Eddy, while William, with a wink at Mrs. Chadwick, turned over the page and began on "C." He went on then, with some ridiculous sketch and jingle to illustrate each letter. For E, he drew a boy, putting under the figure:

> E stands for Eddy, and for him I took
> Pains to compose this entertaining book.

That young man's favorite came with the sixteenth:

> P is a pimple — 'tis a thing which grows
> Sometimes upon a luckless parson's nose.

When William finally finished the alphabet, and presented the pamphlet to the boy, Eddy seized it with eager gratitude and ran off happily to "study his abc's."

"I will net you a silk case to carry it in," his mother called after him. "I don't know how I can thank you," she said to William. "The girls had no trouble, but I was afraid Eddy would never learn a simple thing like the alphabet."

"It isn't so simple at the age of seven," William reminded her; "but seems frightfully stupid work, as I recall. I'm glad if I have succeeded in helping you both out of a bad situation."

"I'm sure Eddy will always remember the Thackeray alphabet!" Mrs. Chadwick was still smiling over William's devices. She wanted to give them a glass of wine, but the two decided they must be on their way if they were to take in any entertainment.

"How about Vauxhall?" Macready suggested outside.

"Vauxhall Gardens, the very thing!" William agreed enthusiastically. And, hailing a cab, they set out for the famous pleasure resort on the Surrey side of the Thames. The lights of Vauxhall could be seen twinkling in the distance soon after they crossed Westminster Bridge and joined the almost unbroken line of carriages travelling toward the gates of the Gardens. Eight thousand oil lamps were strung together down the lanes, between trees, through archways and across pavilions. Lamps of every color, shade, of many different designs and shapes glowed from far away, and became dazzling up close.

Since 1662, when they had first been opened to the public merely to display the beautiful walks and fountains, the gardens had grown in grandeur and entertainment, enhanced by lavish decoration and sumptuous effects, until they had become a fusion of fairyland and carnival.

William and Mac paid their three shilling sixpence at the entrance gate and strolled into the Grand Walk. The orchestra, in its elegant pavilion, was tuning up for the evening's performance.

"Come, we mustn't miss old Simpson," Macready hurried William toward the sound.

They passed in front of a series of small pavilions, each separated by columns, which served as supper boxes for parties wishing to dine at Vauxhall. In some pavilions a gentleman was carving a chicken, or tossing up a salad while the waiter twirled a bottle of champagne in its pail of ice. The boxes were built in semicircles in several parts of the gardens so that diners could take in various entertainments while they ate.

Now, at the blare of trumpets heralding the musical entertainment, groups of people who had been promenading in the Grand and cross walks came thronging to the "grove" to hear the concert. At the second trill of trumpets, a fat, florid, bald-pated showman, resplendent in frilled shirt-front, swallow-tailed coat and shiny knee breeches, made his appearance before the orchestra, smiling urbanely at the crowds.

"You'd think old Simp would buy himself a wig," Mac whispered.

"What? And change his luminous portrait?" William nodded to the colossal likeness of the man in colored lamps, which glittered in the quadrangle back of the orchestra.

"Ssh!" hissed an impatient spectator behind them.

The portly "gentleman" rested his beaver and gold-tipped ebony cane against the balustrade while he waited for such comments and hissings to quiet down. He was C. H. Simpson, for thirty-five years Master of Ceremonies at Vauxhall.

Smoothing out the sheets of paper which contained his address, he began to read in elegant, evenly punctuated tones: "To the most illustrious princes and princesses of the British Empire; to their excellencies the most noble and puissant princes, . . . to all the truly illustrious and noble and distinguished visitors of the Royal Gardens, Vaux-hall . . . "

To all these, and many more, the Master of Ceremonies dedicated the night's offerings before announcing them, one by one, and calling for applause for the artists. The orchestra played works by Haydn, Mozart and Handel. A soprano and a baritone performed solos, the organ's rich tones boomed out in some concerto, and there was a grand finale by all the musicians at once. When the musical program was over, Mr. Simpson bade all Vauxhall guests enjoy themselves at the many different attractions of the gardens. "Don't forget," he lifted his voice over the rustle of dispersing crowds, "the breath-taking cascades will commence in a few minutes, at nine o'clock, till nine-fifteen; and at ten, promptly, the magnificent fireworks."

He had hardly finished speaking when a warning bell sounded. The waiters began announcing to people in the boxes that the display was about to start, and most of the supper-parties rose to join the crowds heading for the famous cascades, or "waterworks," as they were commonly called.

This feature was perhaps the most fantasy-forming of all in the garden, for the sight of myriad lights playing on the scene of the waterfalls never failed to charm the visitor to Vauxhall. Some seasons the cascades depicted a farm and an old mill, round which the water gushed, turning the paddle wheel which sent up a shower of spray. Another year might show a huge rainbow above a mountainous view covered with palm trees, through which the waters rose and fell in glorious color.

"I should never want to come to Vauxhall in the daytime," William observed when the display was over. "What would this place be like without the lamps and the night's veil of magic?"

"Pretty sordid, I can tell you!" Macready laughed.

They went to the bar near the orchestra for a glass of Vauxhall punch, after which they traversed the gravel walks until it was time for the fireworks. As they climbed the steps to the gallery, William espied two young ladies ahead of them, and remarked loudly to Mac: "What is the use, pray, of going to the gallery by ourselves? The fireworks display is no fun without female companionship."

At this one of the girls peeked round, and poked her friend's rib, and they both tittered and pulled their shawls more closely about their shoulders with an air of modesty. But somehow it happened that in the darkness of the gallery there were two vacant seats right beside the two young ladies. William and Mac lost no time in taking them, and during the "ohs" and "ahs," the general squeals of appreciation that accompanied a shower of stars from a bursting rocket or dazzling pinwheel, the four young people became so well acquainted that an invitation to supper for all, on the part of Macready, was eagerly accepted.

When the fireworks had ended, however, and Mac and William descended the steps from the gallery with their fair companions, they were met at the bottom by a fierce-eyed matron who pounced upon their partners.

"Jenny! Amelia! What do you mean by running off to the fireworks alone? Papa and the boys are waiting with supper at the Temple. You know how seldom your father consents to dine in the boxes."

"But mamma, these gentlemen have asked us to . . . , " Amelia, the prettier one, began.

"Never mind the gentlemen!" her mother admonished, with a withering glance in their direction as she hustled her daughters toward the string of pavilions known as the "Temple of Comus."

"Exit, Romance!" Macready performed a professional flourish with his right hand. "Where now, fellow Romeo?"

William laughed. "Serves us right, I suppose. What do you say to another glass of rack punch?"

As they passed in front of a row of boxes, a gentleman with his family in one of them called out: "Macready! I say, Mac!"

Mac turned. "Why, it's Dr. Maginn!" He stepped up to the box to shake hands with the man, who immediately invited them to supper. "Though I must say the ham is so thin as to be invisible, and the coffee blacker than printer's ink," he warned. He was a thin, nervous, wraith-like man, with a wild brilliance to his eyes and a mouth continually set in a satiric smile. Yet there was a pleasantness and geniality in his manner that made him instantly likable. He was shabbily dressed, his neckcloth could have been cleaner, but it did not seem to matter. He introduced his wife, a sweet, quiet, and extremely neat little person, and their small daughter.

Mac, in turn, presented William to the Maginns. "The doctor, you know, writes for 'Fraser's'," he added.

"Yes, of course. I recognized the name." William bowed. "This is a very great pleasure, sir."

Dr. Maginn eyed him sharply. "You are interested in journalism?"

"Yes, in all the arts: writing, drawing, acting . . . "

"You are young," the doctor said decisively. "Not yet of age, I should judge."

"I shall be in a few months!" William told him stoutly.

"Ah. Have some salad, both of you. And, if you enjoy glasses. "Journalism, my lad, is not an art. It could be; it make-believe, a slice of ham. And some of this abominable port." He drained his own, and poured out three fresh should be; but it becomes mere hack-writing under the present circumstances: straining against a dead-line, being grossly underpaid, bowing to the whims of editors and threats of publishers . . . " He stopped and grinned mischievously. "Of course, the profession has its compensations. Don't I see my friend Macready's opening without the price of a ticket? And treat my family to an evening at Vauxhall for scribbling a newspaper account of the patronage here and the entertainment ushered before us by that mincing idiot, Mr. Simpson?"

He talked on, scarcely requiring an answer. He had a facility for apt phrasing that delighted William and prompted him to lead Maginn on and on with questions about the newspaper profession. From there they launched into literature, particularly Homer, a subject on which the doctor surpassed his primary brilliance in a rousing defense of the great Greek against William, who had never felt much enthusiasm for the classical poet.

When the last bite of supper was consumed, and the last drop of "abominable port" drained from the bottle, the two were still deep in discussion.

"Come." Dr. Maginn stood up. "We will see my wife and daughter safely home, and adjourn to Evan's."

"If you go to Evan's, my dear," his wife demurred, "you will stay up half the night and be unable to write tomorrow."

"Don't worry, I won't let him stay too long," Macready reassured her. "I have rehearsal in the morning, and you know I insist upon true acting then as well as in the performance. It takes a vast deal of energy to convince my thick-headed colleagues that they must no more mouth a speech in rehearsal than they would during the show. I need my strength in the morning, too."

"And I, to drag myself to Mr. Taprell's," William put in.

Between them they convinced Mrs. Maginn, and, after depositing her with the little girl at the Maginns' shabby lodgings off Fleet Street, the three gentlemen drove to Evan's, the public house which had become famous as the haunt of literary men, of noblemen, artists — of all who enjoyed Bohemian merrymaking and heated discussion.

They headed for a door back of the main floor of the pub, which led into a narrow room filled with men sitting at a table that ran nearly the length of it. A few of the customers were having supper, others sipped their glasses of brandy-and-water, while the "chairman" of the evening smiled blandly on the proceedings over the tip of a portentous cigar he flourished. Hagden, a voluntary performer, was singing "The Body Snatcher," sitting on a coffin, beside a spade and a candle stuck in a grinning skull. The glasses quivered on the table as the eerie story of this melancholy dirge unfolded.

William and his companions slipped into three empty places quietly so as not to disturb singer or listeners until the ballad was over, for "The Body Snatcher" was one of the highlights at Evan's, and it was not too often that customers could find someone willing to perform. There were no regular singers: visitors "obliged."

When the weird, daring ballad came to a close, a storm of applause and loud cries of "encore!" rewarded the singer. The three newcomers were greeted by the rest of the company, and William and the doctor settled down for a continuation of their discussion. A few, interested in Homer, joined in — journalists, who were friends of Dr. Maginn. Macready after a bit went to talk to Hagden, for he could not keep away from fellow performers, whatever their field. More songs were sung, some by the whole company, and a

political argument concerning the anti-corn laws flared up
and swept the entire table in a blaze of interest. Maginn
became fiery in the cause of reform. "I shall write an editorial tomorrow, an editorial that will burn up the paper
on which it is printed!" He pounded the table till the
glasses shook.

At his words, William felt a sudden thrill, a zeal that he
had not known for some time. To write for a newspaper —
to have the power of rousing the world against the evils of
civilization — that would be a profession! Before he parted
company with Maginn, he made an appointment with the
doctor to visit the offices of "The National Standard," the
newspaper on which he served as critic and chief reporter.
The "Standard" was on shaky legs financially, and many a
week Maginn's salary was not paid, but there were no other
newspaper posts available, and his contributions to "Fraser's"
were hardly enough to support a family.

William spent an entire day with his new friend at the
offices of this press in Fleet Street, the newspaper row of
London. Maginn showed him the mysteries of printing, and
writing lead articles. He took him to the office of the sub-
editor, who sat surrounded by his pots of paste and clippings
scattered over his desk, while, with scissors in hand, he
hunted for more material the "Standard" might use.

As he stood watching the presses revolve, William
breathed in the acrid smell of printer's ink, and some of it
entered his veins. "Do you think the 'Standard' would be
interested in contributions?" he inquired as casually as he
could.

But Maginn knew the signs too well. "A-ha! The virus
has taken hold already, I see. My boy, this newspaper is in
great need of fresh young blood like yours, but how shall
you be paid? There is not even enough for the staff, as it is."

"I see." They had returned to Maginn's office, and William idly fingered the long proof sheets on the desk.

"However," the doctor picked up the top volume from a stack of books, blowing the dust off the cover as he spoke, "we are way behind on reviews. If you wish to take a chance on remuneration, or be content with experience as your pay — "

William did not give him a chance to finish. "I'll do it!" He snatched the volume from Maginn. "I'll write such reviews the public will take note, the circulation will increase, and the publisher will offer me a permanent post on the paper."

"Easy, my boy." Maginn laughed. "Enthusiasm is a necessary ingredient for success, but don't let it carry you too far from reality." He opened the lower drawer and took out a bottle of claret along with two glasses. "Nevertheless, let us drink to your success, no matter what your calling."

"Thank you — and to yours," William returned the compliment.

Maginn shook his head. "It is too late for me, I'm afraid. I am too weak to mend my ways, or I should have been successful long ago."

"You never had the chance!" William defended him loudly. "If I owned a newspaper . . . "

The doctor's indulgent smile made him stop, but as he gathered up an armful of books to read in his "spare time," a notion was born within him that would not die. Why not? Why shouldn't he become a newspaper publisher? In a few months his long-awaited inheritance — the income from the part of his patrimony he had not lost — would begin. He would be a man, allowed to face other men in whatever capacity he chose. And though he knew the fourth estate to be a venturous one, full of hazards, still he would prefer it to that of pleading the law.

He would have to keep on at Taprell's for awhile. There was no reason, however, why he could not merge the two careers. Arthur Buller was studying law and writing magazine articles. Jackie Kemble was now "reading" in the Temple, and writing his book on Anglo-Saxon as he had promised. It was not uncommon for gentlemen who had qualified to maintain offices in the Temple for years while they entered and carried on an entirely different calling. Why shouldn't he do the same?

He confided his plan to Fitz, who came down from Cambridge to attend the marriage of one of his sisters. His friend approved the idea warmly. "It's the sort of thing you should do, Thack. I somehow can't see you as a barrister. You are too much aware of the sadness of humanity, in addition to the gaiety and laughter of it, to spend your time haggling over its laws."

"I could draw cartoons for the paper, also — lampoon some of the things I object to," William mused.

"Of course you can. You are an artist, Willy, and your work should be in the arts."

"What about you, Fitz? Will you contribute to the "Standard?"

The customary irony in Edward's voice grew more pronounced. "And what, pray, would a lazy fellow like me have to offer? You know I am forever merely translating."

"You do much more than translate," William pointed out. "You re-create a work, so that it might well be entirely new. Won't you let me print some of the poems you have done?"

But his friend remained adamant, and since his newspaper ownership was still a nebulous dream, he said no more about it.

But he consulted his parents on the project when they came from Larkbeare for a few days in Town, and found them surprisingly in favor of it.

"Your money will be yours to do with as you choose, William." His mother, lovely in the silk pelisse she was wearing, smiled fondly on him. "I think we can trust your judgment. The editorial policy will be Whig, of course?"

"Of course!"

The Major, who had been turning over the matter by himself, spoke up suddenly. "By Jove, I like it. I like it very much, Bill!"

"I'm glad, sir."

"Yes, indeed." The Major warmed to his subject. "We'll fight for reform. Make it a true Liberal publication — increased franchise, anti-corn-law legislation . . . "

"Henry," his wife said gently, "this is to be William's paper."

"Eh? Oh, sorry, Bill." The Major subsided with a sheepish grin, but William assured him that suggestions would always be welcome.

He spent much time with Dr. Maginn during the following weeks, his determination to purchase "The Standard" should it be for sale when he came of age, growing stronger all the time. He admired the doctor tremendously. The two read Homer together, Maginn pointing out a beauty in the lines which won William over to his great regard for the Greek poet. He introduced William to various figures in the publishing world — to Mr. Gifford, the editor of "The Standard"; Mr. Fraser, editor of "Fraser's," and to a print-seller by the name of Gibbs, who offered to place some of William's caricatures for a share of the profits.

Thackeray's Amusing Drawing of Charles Kemble
as *Henry VIII*

A Page From Thackeray's Sketchbook

The heads of the woman are drawings of
his wife, Isabella

In July, as he had promised, William electioneered with the Bullers, and his observations among the farmers increased his desire to own and operate a liberal newspaper. He went down to the family estate in Cornwall with Charles, who was running for Parliament along with Sir William Molesworth, a wealthy but philosophical radical, who supported the liberal platform of his young neighbor. Mr. and Mrs. Buller, too, shared these political views with their sons. They were charming hosts, who kept a very pleasant house. To William it seemed in every way a perfect country home — attractive, graceful in atmosphere, comfortable.

He rode for twelve hours with Arthur on Wednesday, the day after their arrival, canvassing the farmers of Cornwall. He found much more intelligence and good feeling among them than he had expected. They were not surly or resentful, but sharply aware of the injustices in the existing order, and ready to do what they could, with a limited vote, to change it.

Electioneering lasted three days, ending with a mass assembly that included speeches, luncheon and more speeches. Their campaign was successful, for Charles Buller was elected to the House of Commons when the time came, and gained a brilliant reputation as a speaker in Parliament.

It was after this that Macready burst into William's rooms one day with some startling news. "I just heard Dr. Maginn is in debtor's prison!" His actor's training unconsciously heightened the drama of the announcement.

"What?" William, for once studying articles of law, was out of his chair like a shot. "But I saw him only last week. He said nothing to indicate — "

Macready shrugged his shoulders. " 'The Standard' was hauled down a few days ago. Maginn was out of a job, and his creditors closed in. He never could manage his financial affairs. He's been in prison before, you know."

But William scarcely waited for him to finish before he was on his way out of the door. "That filthy Fleet Street prison — it's an outrage!"

They found the doctor and his small family huddled in a dirty, dank little hole, which Mrs. Maginn had tried to make into livable quarters with the few belongings they were allowed to bring with them. Maginn, quill in hand, was writing furiously at a small table under the only window in the room, a sooty pane which allowed scanty light to penetrate.

He greeted William with a bitter, crooked smile. "You see, my boy, what the newspaper profession is? I'm trying to write my stint for 'Fraser's,' but it won't bring enough to release us — only a mite for rotten food and sour wine." Then, with his usual good nature, he brightened. "Still, as long as one has food for the soul . . . " He put in a period with a flourish.

"It's an insult, a burning shame to send you here!" William brought his big fist down on the makeshift desk. "Maginn, do you think I could buy 'The Standard'?"

And so it was that in May, 1833, William found himself owner and publisher of "The National Standard," whose full title contained the additional words, "and Journal of Literature, Science, Music, Theatricals, and the Fine Arts." His inheritance enabled him to buy the paper, and he immediately hired Dr. Maginn as editor, paying him in advance a sum of five hundred pounds, which permitted him to pay his debts and release the family from the infamous Fleet Street.

"The Standard" was, to be sure, more literary than political, but William saw to it that the editorials were "radical" in flavor. He consulted with the editorial board on policy, wrote articles, theatrical reviews (Macready and the Kembles figured largely in these columns) and now and then inserted a poem. When Maginn — who, he discovered, was a slipshod worker, now brilliant, now careless — failed to come forth with an editorial, William supplied it. He was a very busy young man, too busy for the Bar.

In keeping with his new position of dignity, he bought a pince-nez to wear as he sat in his swivel chair behind his publisher's desk. When he was not working, he stuck it in his left eye like a monocle, the other half just hanging down. His friends, Jackie Kemble for one, liked to rail him about such eccentricities, but he did not mind. Now that he was an entrepreneur in the publishing world, he would indulge all his eccentricities!

At first, with the change of hands, the "Standard" enjoyed a spurt of popularity, but it soon bogged down, and the board met to discuss ways and means of increasing the sale. The suggestion was made that news direct from Europe might do a great deal to heighten the interest in the paper, and before the discussion was well under way, William had appointed himself Paris correspondent.

23

The Paris Correspondent

ONCE HE HAD FOUND suitable lodgings in Paris, William sallied forth to see the sights, this time with an eye for news. First, however, he went to call on the Ritchies. As in London, they had a large comfortable apartment, plus a summer home outside the city, at Les Thermes. The big, cheerful family — there were five children — made William feel at home here as they had in London. The oldest of his cousins, William, was planning on entering Cambridge in a year or two, followed by a law course in the Temple, and was eager for information on both places. But Aunt Ritchie showed more interest in "The National Standard."

"Let your cousin tell us something of his newspaper," she exhorted her son. "Can't you see he is just holding himself in?"

"Am I so obvious, Aunt Ritchie?" William's face grew red.

"Mother means to say that she is more anxious to hear about your purchase than about college," Cousin William thrust in, "and so am I, really, Bill."

"And so are we all," added Charlotte, speaking for the younger Ritchies. She had inherited her mother's kind understanding. Unfortunately, smallpox had disfigured her face a couple of years before and it pained William to see the damage the disease had done.

He told them all about the paper without further insistence, his own enthusiasm mounting under the influence of his sympathetic audience. Life was miraculously simple and rosy at the Ritchies'.

His grandmother Butler, his mother's mother, was not quite so encouraging. William had seen her at Larkbeare, when she came to visit once or twice in the summer. A cantankerous old lady, he thought her — the best-dressed, the neatest old lady in Paris, but selfish and imperious to the last degree.

"And if you fritter your inheritance on any more such schemes, you will soon be ruined, and don't expect me to help you out! If you had entered into some safe business, set up your law practice with some of your money . . ." Mrs. Butler went on berating.

William waited patiently for her to finish, which she did presently, by asking him to go to the Opera, in a manner that was more of an edict than an invitation. "Command performance," he thought humorously, accepting.

His weekly column for the paper did not begin to take up all his time. He wrote satiric pieces as well, trying to improve the morals of the people. He recalled that in speaking to the farmers with Arthur Buller, he had promised to lessen the taxes, provide for their agricultural and commercial interests, and to condemn the infamous slave trade of the West Indian islands. "The Standard" was not exactly the type of paper for such propagandizing but he directed its editorials into liberal channels, and crossed over to London frequently to chart its political course. It gave him a fine sense of importance to feel that a new form of public opinion might be molded by the "Standard." He managed to attend the diplomatic affairs — teas, balls, breakfasts — and, as foreign correspondent, sent home spicy accounts of the great names in both countries. He reviewed French plays and books.

Late in the fall, he received a bid for membership in the Garrick Club, the exclusive organization devoted to the theater and allied arts. No doubt of it, he was becoming a figure in the world. Not that he had much incentive for creative work, writing poetry, or translating it, like Fitz. "This system of newspaper writing spoils one for every other kind of writing," he remarked in one of his letters. But he didn't mind; everything was going so well. "I am happy to say 'The National Standard' is growing into repute."

For all his self-appointed duties and activities, however, he still had time to spare, and found himself turning toward art. He had done several caricatures for Mr. Gibbs, the print-seller, who had asked for more. He could, perhaps, publish a good many with his newspaper connections.

With this in mind, William went to call on John Brine, a lean, lanky, bearded Bohemian, full of affectations, artistic mannerisms, and hospitality. "Come to see me, come to my *atelier*," he had said on being introduced to William by a journalist friend of both, Eyre Evans Crowe, correspondent of "The Morning Chronicle." The Crowes' sixth floor apartment served as a gathering place for writers and artists every Saturday night, with Mrs. Crowe and the children joining in the jokes and songs — the latter usually being started by that lady at the piano. When John Brine learned that Mr. Thackeray had leanings toward art, he was profuse in his invitations, and William not loath to take advantage of them.

Brine's studio was more like a warehouse than the "atelier" William had pictured. Twenty feet high, fifty feet long, and quite bare of usable furniture, it was covered with all sorts of tapestry, old arms, china, carved chairs and cabinets. From a beam across the ceiling hung a broken guitar, a tragi-comic touch. William stood in the doorway surveying the bizarre effect of this conglomeration, while his host, paint-brush in hand, pipe in mouth, stocking-cap over one ear, beckoned him inside.

John Brine was not a good artist, but he was a valiant one. Extremely poor, but exalted by his profession, he made the most of its theatricalities without bothering to master its fundamentals. He lifted his eyes, quoted poetry and stroked his ragged, blond beard as he showed his canvases, filled with splotches of color and minute detail. Though his talent was questionable, he knew the best teachers in Paris, the best times to work in the Louvre, and the best artists among the struggling students.

Before long, William was taking a few lessons, sketching in the great art galleries when he could, and taking part in the pleasures of the Latin quarter. There were true "merry fellows" in the ateliers of Paris, always singing, smoking, fencing, and painting industriously besides. With their wild ways and carefree poverty, they were the happiest people in the world. In Brine's studio one morning, five of them gathered for a late breakfast — five sausages, three loaves and a bottle of wine — and for fifteen sous (threepence apiece), they had a feast. There were no plates or knives; meat was carved by the fingers; the crisp French bread and spicy sausage never tasted so good to William as it did that day. Pipes and stories succeeded the sausage, then songs, and finally, work.

In the midst of this diverting life, word came that the "Standard" was losing ground (and money) steadily, and William was forced to rush back to reality at the London office.

24

Worse Luck Follows Bad

THE BOOKS of the "National Standard" showed figures alarmingly grave. William had lost two hundred pounds to date, and there were debts outstanding. Maginn was proving himself a careless editor, hopelessly impractical.

"We must do something, something to revive the public interest." William paced up and down in front of the editor's desk, where Maginn sat, scribbling furiously, as always, turning out a last-minute manuscript that should have been done before. "The title is too cumbersome, for one thing." He ran his big hand across his hair, and fixed his pince-nez into his left eye pensively, stopping squarely in front of the doctor. "What do you say to 'Literary Representative' in place of all those words?"

"Hm? Eh? Oh! Capital, my boy. Excellent choice." Maginn gave his hearty consent without, William was sure, quite knowing it.

At the special board meeting which was called, the title, "The National Standard and Literary Representative" was adopted, along with a rise in price from two to threepence. The measures injected new life for a time. William moved into a small house belonging to his parents, at 18 Albion Street, to be close enough to keep an eye on the proceedings in Fleet Street. He would not return to Paris until all was well.

But by the end of the year, there was no reason for him to return as foreign correspondent: "The Standard" lost ground steadily after its brief spurt, and was continuing to lag behind other newspapers in popularity at such a rate it seemed foolhardy to go on. William, resigning himself to the fate of his ill-starred project, called the executive board and chief stockholders together for a conference. After a review of the gloomy facts, followed by a short discussion, the company decided to disband, since no one wished to invest further capital. A few days later, in February, 1834, the sorry banner of "The Standard" was hauled down forever. The newspaper ownership had lasted only eight months.

Dr. Maginn, clearing out his desk before it was removed, piling up his papers, pens, blue-pencils, and clippings, tried to console William, who wandered aimlessly about the office, somewhat bewildered by the suddenness of the final downfall.

"At least, Thackeray, you've weathered the worst of the disease. From now on, you should be immune!"

William shook his head. "I was ready to invest more money if any of the rest had been willing."

"The germ has gone deeper than I thought!" The doctor stood up. "Well, this is a business of black and white in more ways than one. Don't be discouraged, my boy. In the publishing world, your fortunes may rise and fall as regularly as the sea. When the outlook is blackest, white hopes will come and turn into reality. Am I not the perfect example? Didn't your fling at folly save me from debtor's prison?" He grew more serious. "Whatever befalls either of us, I shall never forget your help at that time."

"You make me feel that it has all been worthwhile, in spite of our failure to keep going." William, somewhat embarrassed, fingered the lead cuts stacked on a bench. "What are you going to do for your next position?"

The erstwhile editor shrugged his shabbily-clad shoulders. "As I told you, something will turn up. What of your plans?"

William weighed a small lead type in his hand. "I don't know yet what I shall do. But of one thing I'm certain: I shan't go back into law — not after being so alive as I have been during the past months instead of a half-mummified drudge like my neighbor Bleek in the Temple. Perhaps I shall merely live off my income, but I shall live!"

Before he could make up his mind as to his next move, however, a letter came to Albion Street from Larkbeare, advising him to come immediately. There were rumors of a huge East Indian bank failure, in which they might all be involved.

When he entered the square hall at home and found them all waiting for him, William saw with one look that the rumors must have materialized in the short time since he had left London. He kissed his mother, and went into the drawing-room with her, followed by the Major and Mary. He tried to keep up a running fire of small talk about his trip, but he soon ceased. They were all too heavy with gloom.

He placed his hands on his mother's shoulders with a gentle shake. "All right, let's have it straight off. There was a bank failure, and we are ruined, are we not?"

"Yes, William." His mother's voice was low.

He was somewhat surprised at her ready confirmation. "Really?" He turned to Polly and his stepfather. "I can scarcely believe it."

The Major, too, was grave. "It's quite true, Bill. Hundreds of British families have suffered steep losses, I understand."

"But how? What happened?"

The Major explained that through a series of bad investments, the banks had lost much of the shareholders' money. After tea, he got out the papers that had been sent, and showed William the figures. William's loss was more complete than his parents', while Polly's inheritance had luckily remained intact. From the remains of his fortune, William would receive a dividend of no more than twenty-five pounds quarterly.

"Hardly enough to provide me with cigars, but at least I can't blame myself for the loss. In a way it's rather a relief," he concluded cheerfully.

Surprisingly, his grandmother Butler offered him a chance to live with her in Paris as soon as she heard of the disaster. She was alone and could easily accommodate him. He decided to accept her invitation for awhile at least — in spite of a certain uneasiness over her disposition. He could, perhaps, perfect his skill in painting enough to earn his way from it. First, however, he would go up to London to set his affairs in order there.

From 18 Albion Street, he wrote to Edward Fitzgerald, including in the letter news of the bank failure. Fitz, with his usual loyalty, responded by coming from Ipswich immediately.

"I'd have asked you to Wherstead, but my sisters and brothers, with their respective husbands, wives and children are there for the season," he hastened to explain, "and I leave to your imagination the amount of privacy we should have. Now to the facts!"

He would not be satisfied until William had given them all as they sat over their pipes the night he arrived. Before they retired he commissioned his friend to do sixteen water-color illustrations for his copy of "Undine." "I have been wanting to order illustrations for some time," he said; "and as soon as I learned you had the leisure, I thought of you for the assignment. That is really why I came to Town."

"I don't doubt it." William smiled at Fitz fondly. "You

humbug! You are more capable of doing the proper water-
colors than I."

"Rot. My work is weak and ill-defined. You can do the
sketches while I'm here. Only see to it the price isn't too
steep!"

He would not listen to a refusal, so for the next two or
three days, he and William sat talking and smoking while
the drawings for "Undine" took shape. Fitz was warm in his
approval of "Thack's" plan to study art seriously in Paris.
"I think one of us ought to become established in a career,"
he said with his ironic inflection, "and I cannot name a finer
one than painting."

They spoke of the great masters, Rubens, and Raphael,
Rembrandt and da Vinci. They walked the streets in the
warm, spring evenings, visited with the Kembles, and at the
actor's invitation, took in Macready's fine performance of
"Macbeth."

It was a lighthearted interlude for William, singularly free
of financial cares. Indeed it was a blessing not to have any
money to worry about! "I believe that I ought to thank
heaven for making me poor," he wrote to his parents, "as it
has made me much happier than I should have been with
money."

25

The Elysian Fields

WILLIAM'S FEARS about his grandmother were well-founded. Even now, as he bent over the desk, busy with a letter to his mother, she was harping on the late hours he kept, his rag-tag companions . . .

"Not that I begrudge you a good time, William. You are young, and need a little recreation now and then. But there is no need to carouse around half the night, and with those odious fellows." She was mostly concerned with the respectability of his company. She possessed a certain warmth of heart, hidden under a cloak of asperity. There was a "delicate benevolence" in her, William wrote.

> If I did not praise her, I should abuse her [he continued], as I am at this moment writing under the stripes of her satire, and the public expression of her wrath. . . . I have been working hard at the Louvre, and begin tomorrow at the Life Academy. I have no time for original drawing, but it is just as well. Studying great old painters puts one sadly out of conceit with one's mean little efforts.

At this point his grandmother's remarks grew so cutting he could stand it no longer, and he left the room right in the middle of them. He would go to the Ritchies'.

His aunt, of course, asked him to stay for dinner (he had counted on her invitation), and afterward he and William Ritchie went to the opera together. What a godsend to have his favorite relatives in Paris! Hardly a day passed that he did not take his evening meal with them. Aunt Ritchie's mellow laugh was like an ointment spilling over the nervous irritation caused by his grandmother.

Another retreat he sought more and more was the Crowe family's sixth floor apartment — "the Crowes' nest," he called it. He formed the habit of dropping in early on Saturday nights before the party — so early that he was usually in time for dinner. After awhile it was an accepted custom, and he would amuse the children with comic drawings as they awaited summons to the table. He invented a series that ran for weeks, which he called "The Adventures of the Count," and which were caricatures in art and narrative of John Brine, who had taken himself off to Spain to paint. Such escapades as William thought up for him, not even the hyperbolic artist himself would have invented!

But in spite of these pleasant harbours, life with Mrs. Butler proved rough sailing. When he received a card from Fitz and Alfred Tennyson, who were taking a trip together in the lake country of Scotland, he wished he might be with them. His grandmother was really becoming intolerable.

At last he could bear her tirades no longer, and on June 11, 1835, moved into lodgings at no. 1, Rue de Beaux Arts, a dingy little hotel, it was true, but he much preferred the calm quiet of his cobweb-smeared walls to his grandmother's pretty apartment where a storm usually raged. For a brief period, with many hand-written scoldings, Mrs. Butler sent him a small stipend once a week, but this, too, he rejected. After that they were better friends than at any time they were together. The old lady, like Dr. Russell at Charterhouse, was not so fearsome once you got outside her province. He felt much as he had when he became a day-boy, or when he had left his school altogether. Just as he had enjoyed going back to Charterhouse for Founder's Day each year, so he walked stoutly up to his grandmother's three days a week to be scolded. The matriarch's masterly invective amused him when he didn't have to listen to it all the time. What a character she would make in a novel! When she came to see him, as she did quite often, they got on remarkably well, in spite of the way she sniffed at his shabby rooms, sitting on the edge of her chair for fear of bugs.

It was a rather lonely existence, for all that he enjoyed the easy companionship of his artist colleagues. He was beginning to know the pinch of poverty, which, though it never seemed to trouble the other students, bit into his tastes sharply. His waistcoats were worn, and he had no money for new ones. He could not buy theater tickets, or expensive dinners, or champagne any more. He had not even enough to pay the doctor when he fell from his mule during a mountain excursion some of them took, and broke his nose once again! But he made up his mind not to ask for a penny more than the allowance his parents sent every month. They were in straitened circumstances also. To save expenses, they had given up Larkbeare, moving the household, including the Goldsworthys, to 18 Albion Street. He would work hard, and be content to drink small beer, walk the boulevards or visit relatives and friends for his entertainment; but it was not very exciting.

Toward the end of August, he was returning from the Louvre, paintbox under his arm, walking down the Champs-Elysées where the horse chestnuts were already turning brown, wondering how he should spend the evening, when he ran into Daniel Maclise, an artist friend who was on the staff of "Fraser's."

"It looks as though I shall have to alter my masterpiece, now that you have a mustache!" Maclise had made a portrait of William the year before, and appeared to resent the fine line of hair that had come to grace William's upper lip in the past month. "You shouldn't have done it, Thack!"

"Merely a whim, Maclise. After all, one must have something for diversion."

"Right you are. And what are you doing this evening?"

"Nothing in the world. I expect to partake of a lonely dinner in my rooms, but if you care to join me — "

"Stop there. Why don't you come with me? My pension has a fairly decent cuisine, and I believe you will like some of the boarders."

"You need say no more. I accept with pleasure." William crooked his elbow, Maclise linked his arm through, and they walked off together toward the boardinghouse, located in a little street just off the Champs-Elysées.

The pension, run by a French woman, contained, like most fashionable — or "respectable" — places in Paris, a majority of Anglo-Saxons, Irish, British, Scotch; and a sprinkling of Nordics and Latins — a German, two Italians and occasionally, a Spaniard. Only Madame Duboise, the proprietress, was French. English was commonly spoken. Madame presided over her long table, which nearly filled the dining-room, with the air of a harassed schoolmarm who was ardently hoping nothing went amiss. Most of the places were filled when William and his host filed in, taking the two most convenient ones still vacant.

Maclise introduced his guest to their neighbors. "Mr. Thackeray, may I present Mrs. Shawe, and her daughter, Miss Isabella?"

William started to acknowledge with the usual bow, but stopped short at the lovely appearance of the young girl, and sat staring at her, enchanted, forgetful of her mother and the rest. Isabella Shawe was like a rosebud, full of sweetness and a spring-like freshness. She wore her soft, light-brown hair parted in the middle, and taken gently back to a cluster of curls held by a high Spanish comb — a charming frame for her sweet, round face, with its dreamy eyes, pert little nose, and full red lips. He wanted to paint her at once; he wanted to go on gazing at her like this forever.

He heard her voice, clear and tinkling, respond to the introduction, and then he was brought up sharply by the raspy sound of her mother's: "How d'ye do, young man. Will you passez-moi le beurre, s'il vous plait?"

Could this yellow-faced, beak-nosed, hawk-eyed old harpy actually be Isabella Shawe's mother? He could find no resemblance. True, Mrs. Shaw's coiffure was like her daughter's, done with the high Spanish comb, but how ridiculous it was on her! He had the itch to use his drawing-pencil again, but this time in caricature. Everything about the girl seemed dainty, sweet, and delightful — everything about her mother coarse, sour and disagreeable. To be sure, he might be wrong in jumping to such a conclusion merely on meeting the Shawes. He would have to become better acquainted with them before passing judgment; it was no more than fair. He would have to patronize Madame Duboise's boardinghouse frequently!

"Are you staying in Paris long, Mr. Thackeray?" the clear, tinkling voice asked.

"I am living here in order to study art. I have been a newspaper correspondent until recently."

"Where are you staying, Mr. Thackeray?" the raspy voice asked.

"Number one, Rue de Beaux Arts."

"What newspaper did you write for, Mr. Thackeray?" came the melodic voice again.

" 'The National Standard.' "

A dowager

"And why did you give it up, may I ask?" followed the harsh one.

So it went throughout the meal, first one questioned him, then the other, until William's ears were buzzing with the alternate harmony and dissonance. On the one hand, he felt as if he were carrying on a delightful tête à tête; on the other, as if he were the subject of an inquisition. Eventually, the dinner was over, the "guests" trooped out of the *salle à manger,* and into the front salon.

William, elbowed by his friend, had to meet the other boarders, but with a skillful maneuver, managed to find himself a seat on the sofa beside Isabella. How small and delicate she was! what a diverting laugh she had, like little bells pealing out suddenly! He was not sure what they talked about — commonplace things, no doubt — but he had never had such an exhilarating conversation with anyone. He felt almost lightheaded, and his heart was a quivering bubble.

Two gaunt English girls, whom Isabella called familiarly, Tommy and Clark, rattled off a few sonatas on Madame's somewhat rusty piano for the benefit of the company. Under cover of the noise they created, William was able to throw a compliment or two in among his conventional remarks about the warm weather, Paris, Ireland (the Shawes' home), and not be heard by Isabella's mother. He had an idea his attentions would not be exactly welcome.

When the two performers at the piano had finished their repertoire, they called on Isabella to sing. At first she refused, blushing, saying she had no talent, and why didn't her friends be quiet. But they coaxed her, and her mother, with a gesture of irritation, urged sharply, "Come, Isabella, don't be so shy. I'm sure we all wish to hear you, and you have been sitting around long enough." She cast a suspicious glance at William.

He was forced to add his plea, though he did not want her to leave the sofa, for fear she might not return. "Do give us a song, Miss Shawe. I'm anxious to hear you. Judging from this clamor, you must have a voice well worth listening to."

"If you wish, I will sing for you," she said very softly as she went past him.

"I will sing for you," she had said. If she possessed a screech like a magpie, he would deem it beautiful after those words. But happily Isabella Shawe could sing like a lark, in high, clear, lilting tones. Her sweetness and purity shone out as well, and now and then her Irish humor, so that her audience could not help being charmed. No wonder they had all begged her to sing. He was more and more taken with this bit of a girl.

Luckily, her mamma was engaged for a foursome of whist when the songs were over, and Isabella came back to the sofa without her notice. William stayed as late as he dared without overstepping the bonds of propriety. But before he went home, he made arrangements with Madame to eat at her boardinghouse three times a week, so he would be sure of seeing Isabella again.

"Will you save a place next to you at table on Wednesday?" he whispered as they said good-bye. "I shall be here."

"If I can, I will," she returned softly. "Come early. Perhaps we can go in together."

He hardly breathed until Wednesday. Then he put on the best of his remaining waistcoats, gave the bootblack a sou to shine his cracked leather shoes, and got out his only clean pair of gloves in order to appear as well-groomed as possible before the incomparable Isabella and her dragon-toothed mother. He had left the Louvre early to prepare for this second meeting, which he felt to be deeply important. Not even in Weimar had he been so excited at the thought of a young lady — and over a chit of an Irish lass "no bigger than my thumb!" he laughed out loud. But he fixed his pince-nez cockily in his left eye, and smoothed his newly-acquired mustache to give him confidence. Then, before the sun had quite gone down across the Seine, he was taking his way along the Champs-Elysées to Madame's boarding-house.

He arrived before the pensioners had assembled, and finding no one in the front salon nor the *salle à manger,* he strolled out through a door which led to the inner court, where a very pretty little garden afforded the guests a cool retreat. Here, seated on one of the wrought iron benches among the late summer flowers, was Isabella Shawe, quite alone, reading one of Maria Edgeworth's novels.

He came up behind the bench. "Do you enjoy Miss Edgeworth, Miss Shawe?"

"Oh!" She turned around. "How you startled me, Mr. Thackeray. Yes, I like her novels very much. Don't you?"

"Not much." With his long legs, he stepped over the bench and sat down next to her. "If you read English novels, read the best — Henry Fielding's."

"Fie, Mr. Thackeray, 'Tom Jones' is not for young girls."

"What do you wish?" he demanded. " 'Nice' novels, as the saying goes? Sticky sentimental ones, without the substance of truth? I think Fielding is merely honest, candid. How his satire bites the thick skin of our smug society! Do you believe the world isn't full of blackguards, cutthroats, cheats, liars and thieves? That the upper classes are by nature any different from the lower? Can you believe that the world is all sweetness and light?" He glared at her in his vehemence, so that she drew back, wide-eyed. And seeing her small, round face, full of slightly fearful wonderment, he softened, his whole expression changing suddenly. "Forgive me, of course you can!" He put his big hand over her two small ones, folded in her lap. "Anyone as sweet, and kind, and innocent as you . . . "

At this point they heard a harsh clucking from the doorway of the pension. There stood Mrs. Shawe, arms akimbo. "Tsk, tsk, tsk! Isabella, what are you doing out in the garden alone with a gentleman at this hour? I am ready for dinner, and you have not even begun your toilette. Come in, this instant. — Good evening, Mr. Thackeridge," she added coldly.

"Thackeray, Madam," William corrected her as he rose and gave Isabella his arm. He could not imagine how she would be able to improve on her present appearance, but deference to elders demanded that she obey her mother. But how vulgar the old lady was — not to recall one's name, perhaps purposely, to make him seem insignificant, the she-deevil! He passed her by without looking at her, took Isabella to the foot of the staircase, and went into the parlor to wait for her.

Because of this little incident, unfortunately for him, he did not get to sit beside her at the table. Mrs. Shawe herded the girl into the dining-room directly she came down, and saw to it that the places on both sides of them were taken. William, entering with Maclise, was disappointed, but considered the chance rendezvous in the garden well worth this defeat. As a matter of fact, he could see Isabella better from the other side of the table, in the chair directly across from hers. He proceeded to gain this vantage point, casting the merest grin of triumph at Mrs. Shawe. And in spite of that lady's maneuvers, he succeeded in remaining by her daughter through most of the evening.

War had been declared, and from this time onward, the battle raged. Mrs. Shawe was the widow of Colonel Matthew Shawe, who, after their marriage in Doneraile, County Cork, took her to India, where he had been appointed Military Secretary to the Marquess of Wellesley. When her husband died, Mrs. Shawe had brought her family to Paris, where they could live decently on the small army pension, and where, she thought, her daughters should have greater possibilities to make fine matches. Jane was still a child, but Isabella, the oldest of four (two girls and two boys), had reached an eligible age, and her mother was not going to allow her to throw away her beauty on any ardent but penniless admirer. Suspicious of all young men, she had watched William warily, noticing the way he had stared at Isabella from the first.

The self-righteous woman wasted no time in finding out

all she could about "Mr. Thackeray," and what she discovered she did not like. A poverty-stricken art student and
writer was not exactly the sort she had planned for her
daughter to marry, and while he might not have any such
idea in mind, she saw the signs, and hastened to discourage
him from the beginning in every way she could. There were
brief periods, in the evenings that followed, when she was
civil toward William, but for the most part, she was cold,
sarcastic, even rude to him.

He was undaunted, however, and came to the boardinghouse regularly three times a week to take his dinner. He
wangled tickets to the Opera from one of his newspaper
friends, and escorted mother (which propriety demanded)
and daughter to a performance of "Don Giovanni." No be-
jewelled lady in the tiers of private boxes gilded and lined
with red plush made a more beautiful picture than Isabella,
her round, white shoulders gleaming from the dropped neck-
line of her gown, her Spanish comb lending a stateliness to
her small, perfectly-shaped head. A pity one had to look at
her mother occasionally!

By the end of September, no more than a month after he
had met her, William was hopelessly in love with Isabella
Shawe, though he had not dared to show his feeling openly.
When he came to his little room in his hotel after leaving the
boardinghouse, he could think of nothing but her and wish
he were back in the house off the Champs-Elysées. It was
truly the Elysian Fields for him! He was in such a state, he
could not refrain from writing home about it:

My whole seyn, etre, or being is bouleversé or capsized — I
sleep not, neither do I eat, only smoke a little, and build
castles in the clouds. I am so busy spending the evening
uttering the tenderest of sentiments, God knows how it will
end. I will, if I can, bolt before I have committed myself
for better or worse. But I don't think I shall have the power.

He was quite sure he would not. He could hardly work for sighing over Isabella. Instead of copying the great masters, he concentrated on a portrait of her, and sketched her wherever he found a space — on margins of letters, on programs, on backs of envelopes or menus. Now and then he drew a monstrous caricature of her mother, which Isabella thought "too bad" of him, though she did chuckle over them.

He had done a series of satiric sketches on ballet dancers, which he had entitled, "Flore et Zephyr." They told a ludicrous story in pictures, clever enough for publication, his friends told him. Their encouragement gave him the boldness to try his luck with various publishers during the fall and winter. If he were to be the author of a book, which he could shove under Mrs. Shawe's beak nose, perhaps she would not look down it at him any more. Her respect, he felt sure, would make a great difference in his progress with Isabella, which was much too slow to suit him. He hardly ever saw her alone, and he had the impression that her mother discredited him in her daughter's eyes as soon as he left the boardinghouse at night. A book in his name might quiet her clacking tongue.

But although he approached a good many, he did not find a publisher until the middle of February, 1836, and the book would not be out until spring. He could scarcely restrain himself from shouting the good news at once, but he held back. He wanted to surprise Isabella with the first copy.

It was April before he was able to do so. Carrying the slim volume in his hand, he found her in the little court garden again, prodding the earth around Madame's tulips. The sun, breaking through the clouds after an April shower, shone on the golden lights in her brown hair, and set them gleaming.

"Isabella!" He came toward her, holding out the book. She rose, and pulled off her gloves to take it. "Oh,

William! "Your 'Flore et Zephyr' — you did get it published! I'm so glad."

They had called each other by their given names quite without knowing it. He took a step closer to her, and ——

What Mrs. Shawe, coming in search of her daughter a second time, beheld in the garden caused her to scream out, nearly fainting against the door frame, while Madame Duboise came on the run with the smelling salts.

"*Qu'est-ce que c'est? Qu' avez-vous?* What is the matter with you, Madame?" The proprietress applied her bottle generously.

Mrs. Shawe could only gasp, as she pointed at the court: "That detestable young man, daring to kiss my daughter!"

26

Storm and Sunshine

WILLIAM AND ISABELLA were in love. As he said, he had been "building castles in the clouds" since September, but Isabella had only recently begun to return his feeling. With the second incident in the garden, both of them openly declared themselves. They were, in fact, engaged to be married.

The attachment, however, did not have the blessing of Mrs. Shawe, who continued trying to break it off, or at least to discourage Isabella from going through with it. "I don't understand how you could fall in love with that flat-nosed Mr. Thackering," she would say deprecatingly. "Such a great, unattractive gawk."

Isabella, looking distressed and uncomfortable, only said, "Thackeray, mother," and resumed her needlework.

"Yes, a mighty peculiar name, too. Well, mark my words, young lady, if you marry him you'll have nothing but poverty and unhappiness. Do you think an idle, good-for-nothing artist-writer will ever make a name for himself?"

"William has already had a book published." Isabella held up her copy of "Flore et Zephyr." "And don't forget, he owned a newspaper."

"Which he lost through mismanagement." Mrs. Shawe pushed the book down with her bony, yellow hand. "All I can say is you need not expect a dowry from me."

"We don't. All we want is your consent," Isabella said calmly.

"Well, I shan't give it!" Mrs. Shawe flared angrily.

"Please, mother —," Isabella would plead.

William's battle, it was clear, was only half won. His grandmother showed little more sympathy than Mrs. Shawe toward his plans.

"All this potter about being in love!" She rattled the tea things fiercely as she fixed a cup for him during one of his duty calls. "You cannot afford to fall in love, William."

He sputtered, taking the first sip. "Cupid doesn't consult one's pocketbook, grandmother!"

"Obviously not," she said dryly. "And I daresay at your age you can't dodge his dart, but you don't have to take it seriously! The wound need not be fatal. I know what a pinched income can do to a marriage, my son," she finished more quietly. "It is not pretty."

Once again he was aware that Mrs. Butler sheltered a soft heart under her crusty armor of sarcasm, but she gave little indication of it, and would offer no real encouragement to him.

He took Isabella to visit the Ritchies, feeling quite sure he would receive moral support from them. He presented his fiancée proudly, "The diminutive part of me, Aunt Charlotte, Uncle John."

"And quite the prettiest, I should say." His aunt came forward and pressed Isabella's cheek with hers. "Welcome to the home of your future relatives, my dear. We've always kept a place reserved for Billy here, and I expect we can find one for you."

"Won't require more than an inch or two, I judge." Mr. Ritchie held out his hand. "How do you do, my dear. Join the family, if you can stand the confusion."

"Thank you both," Isabella said gratefully. "William says I am not to worry, but sometimes it seems to me my mother will never give her consent, and the whole world appears to be against it."

The young Ritchies were loudly indignant at the idea of Mrs. Shawe objecting to their favorite cousin. Little Emily, the "baby," who was eight, piped, "Cousin Bill is the best, because he always draws pictures," and William Ritchie was of the opinion that the couple should elope if necessary.

His mother was against such rash action. "I'm sure things will work out for you, and if you wish, you can spend your honeymoon at Les Thermes." The offer of their summer home was seconded by Mr. Ritchie, and by the time they said good-bye, Isabella and William felt much more light-hearted about their future.

The Crowes, too, came forward with friendly comfort and assistance. They were delighted with Isabella, whom William brought to one of the Saturday night gatherings. John Brine, just back from Spain, wished to paint her immediately, and the whole company was charmed with her singing.

"By Jove, Thackeray, you've brought a nightingale to the Crowes' Nest!" their host exclaimed, applauding her song.

Everyone in this cheery bohemian circle was of the opinion the two should be married as soon as possible. "Don't wait till you're old," Mr. Crowe said. "Thack is beginning to show a few grey hairs already." (It was true, though he was not yet twenty-five.) "Mrs. C. and I have weathered many an economic storm and so can you." He thought a moment. "I may be able to get you a place as correspondent for the 'Morning Chronicle,' if you like . . ."

"*If* I like!" William jumped up and wrung his friend's hand. "Crowe, if you knew how much a regular income meant to me just now — I should never be able to thank you enough."

"I'll write the London office when I send in my story to-morrow," Crowe said, smiling.

Later, as they bowled toward the boardinghouse in an ancient fiacre, William took advantage of the offer and the spring night to press his case. "You see, Toby" (this was one of many nicknames he had given Isabella; sometimes he called her "Trot" or "Puss" or "Tobykins"), "there is no need to put off our wedding because of a small obstacle like an adequate income. As long as we have a few friends it will come our way. I shall soon gain a reputation for myself, and publishers will be asking for my work!"

"I hope so, William, but in the meantime — "

"In the meantime, we shall be married and happy the whole day through." He moved closer to prove his point.

When he reached home, he wrote to William Jerdan, a member of the Garrick Club, who was the editor of "The Literary Gazette," asking for a little "puff" on "Flore et Zephyr." If a few critics would favor him with puffs on his initial work, it would go far toward establishing his name. And if Crowe succeeded in securing a place for him on the "Morning Chronicle" — He went to sleep in an easier frame of mind than he had since he and Isabella became engaged.

But the weeks dragged by, and the marriage did not take place. Mrs. Shawe was domineering; her daughter very young and easily influenced, a combination which did not help William's cause. He received an approving half-column in the "Gazette," but the position on the "Chronicle" showed no signs of materializing.

His future mother-in-law was so disagreeable at the dinner-table that he stopped taking his evening meal at the board-inghouse. He and Isabella would meet every day at noon in a little park at the Place Vendome, where a fountain splashed in the sun, and small boys played marbles on the stone walk. Isabella would usually bring one of her little brothers, who

served as her excuse to leave her mother's side. Here William
would pour out his heart while the fountain sang and the
small boys shouted at their play and the busy parade of
people hurried by on the boulevard. Occasionally, if her
mother had a headache, or did not see her leave, Isabella
would slip away alone for their rendezvous, and the two
would go walking in the Bois de Boulogne, where the horse
chestnut trees with candelabra-like blossoms let fall a little
shower of white flowerlets around their shoulders. Sometimes they went to Terre's Tavern, for William must have
Isabella share his taste for bouillabaisse.

"What is it like?" she asked the first time.

"Well, let's see . . . " He wanted to assure her.

> This bouillabaisse a noble dish is —
> A sort of soup, or broth, or brew,
> Or hotch-potch of all sorts of fishes,
> That Greenwich never could outdo;

"Oh, William!" Her laugh tinkled below his ear. "But
what is in it?"

> Green herbs, red peppers, mussels, saffron,
> Soles, onions, garlic, roach, and dace:
> All these you eat at Terres' tavern,
> In that one dish of bouillabaisse!

He spread his big hands out before her. "There! I told
old Fitz a ballad could be composed to such a concoction,
and I've made a start. Some day I shall write the rest. In the
meantime, let us discuss the subject thoroughly." He indi-
cated the waiter, a pencil-slim Parisian with a waxed mustache, who approached just then, smiling above the two
smoking dishes. And "discuss" it they did, down to the last
spoonful.

But these occasions were rare, and usually William had to

be content with a few moments of anxious meeting each day. And then one morning he received a brief note that threatened even this. Isabella thought they had better stop seeing each other for a time. Her mother had convinced her that it would be unwise to go on as they were. He was hurt, angry and helpless. If only the post on "The Morning Chronicle" would come through, or any other, no matter what. He wrote an angry reply, followed it with a contrite apology, fussed and fumed for several days, and above all, regretted his lost time at Cambridge. Why didn't the English educational system provide a more practical course in higher learning? Why was so much emphasis placed upon social activities, upon the art of becoming a "gentleman"? And oh, why had he gambled away his patrimony? As he sulked over his "dear Time's waste," he realized that more of it was slipping through his fingers. And then a letter came from his stepfather which caused William to throw a few clothes into a bag and hurry across the Channel to 18 Albion Street.

For some months the Major had been negotiating to form a stock company for the purchase of "The Public Ledger," a political newspaper on its last legs. He intended to call it "The Constitutional" and turn it into an ultra-liberal organ with such policies as: entire freedom of the press, extension of popular suffrage, vote by ballot, shorter duration of Parliament, and equality of civil rights and religious liberties. The Major, as chairman of the company, would now be able to carry out all his pet political ideas as he had longed to do on "The National Standard." His principal motive in the venture, however, was to provide William with a job in the field of journalism.

Both the Major and Mrs. Carmichael Smyth thought that William "could not do better than to marry," but they realized that he must have a regular income or he would never be able to overcome Mrs. Shawe's objections. His step-father spoke confidentially to him over their cigars.

"Now that the stock company has been formed, our paper can begin operations at once, and if I were you I should marry as soon as possible. Otherwise Mrs. Shawe may trick you out of it." He hesitated, blowing out a thin line of blue smoke. "But I think you should wait until the dinner at Mr. Noke's; at that time our staff will be organized."

This was a grand affair at the lawyer's, where William met the directors and editors of the new journal. Douglas Jerrold, a well known reviewer, was to be dramatic critic, and William, Paris correspondent. Major Carmichael-Smyth turned down an offer of two hundred pounds a year for his services as chairman. His only interest was that William be employed on the paper.

"My father's conduct to me in this Paper business has been very noble," William praised him in a letter to Isabella late that night. How many men, he wondered, would be as kind and indulgent to a stepson as the Major had always been? How understanding he was, too. Thinking of the talk they had had together, William, with a sudden resolve to be "firm," as the Major had suggested, put down boldly: "I don't mean to give up seeing you. It is arranged that I am to come back to Paris and have four hundred and fifty pounds a year. So look at the furniture shops and the wedding clothes." Surely anyone would know from this that he was serious about an early marriage, even the indomitable Mrs. Shawe!

Fitzgerald, who came to London as soon as he heard his friend was in Town, also urged William to maintain his stand. The two talked one whole afternoon of pictures, books and Isabella, when it was plain to Edward that William was hopelessly in love.

"Since you feel the way you do, don't delay, Thack," he advised. "See what a crusty bachelor I am becoming. I don't like it."

"Well?" William smiled.

"Well, I cannot find anyone who would be content with Boulge cottage life, and I am already too set to change my ways." He still spent his days studying, translating, polishing his transcriptions. He rarely saw more than two or three people. "But you have found one with whom you want to share your life. Don't throw away the opportunity by postponing it."

All his friends, and even his acquaintances, rallied warmly around him. Mary had sent out fifty invitations for a tea celebrating his arrival. All his friends came — the Kembles, the Bullers, Macready and Fitz — as well as many acquaintances like the Garrick Club members. He met with such cordiality and kindness even from those whom he thought did not care a straw about him that he felt strong and sure of himself at last, not mean and inferior, as he had all these months under Mrs. Shawe's withering blasts. And although he wrote to Isabella: "Are you willing and ready to give up your home . . . to share the fate of a sulky grey-headed old fellow with a small income and a broken nose?" he nevertheless considered himself worthy of the girl he had chosen. In the warm-hearted, approving atmosphere at home his courage expanded until he determined to whisk Isabella off to the bishop's residence as soon as he returned to Paris. Wouldn't he be foreign correspondent for "The Constitutional," with four hundred and fifty pounds a year to his name? How could there be any further objections?

But he reckoned without Mrs. Shawe's obstinacy, and it was several months, punctuated by brief, stormy periods of separation, before she finally capitulated, grudgingly bestowing her consent with a few sour words.

They were more than enough for William and Isabella, however, who flew to make the necessary arrangements. On August 20, 1836, almost a year to the day after they met, they were married in the House of the British Ambassador in Paris. Bishop Luscombe, the English chaplain, read the ceremony, uniting William Makepeace Thackeray and Isabella Gettin Creagh Shawe "with the consent of her mother," who looked on with a dour countenance, while the little bride's heart fluttered, and the tall bridegroom with the broken nose boomed out joyfully, "I do."

27

The Long Climb Begins

THE YOUNG COUPLE were very happy. They had accepted the Ritchies' invitation and spent a delightful month at Les Thermes, and now they were settled in a small apartment in Paris.

William at last felt himself a man, with a man's responsibilities and sense of importance. As he read over his first article which appeared in "The Constitutional," September 19, his chest swelled, and he said to Isabella, "This marks the beginning, Toby. From now on I shall climb until I reach the top, with you beside me."

And Isabella, smiling at him as she dusted the piano, agreed calmly, "Of course you will reach your goal, and I mean to do all I can to help you."

"Dear little Puss, I'm sure you are the best wife in the world!" William rose from the sofa where he had been stretched out reading, and went over to her. "I never knew a purer mind, or a better temper, or a warmer heart."

He had punctuated each of these compliments with a kiss, and would have kept on, but Isabella waved him off with the feather duster. "One of the things I plan to do is to remind you to work," she said with Irish impishness. "You still have an article to write today. Remember?"

William, with a deep sigh and a mock expression of being abused, crossed to his desk, where he pretended to resign himself to his job, but he was soon scribbling away so rapidly, so intently, that one could see it was no chore to him. He was, indeed, concerned with more than his daily stint as Paris correspondent. He had schemes for a dozen ways to increase his income now that he was a married man with a wife to support. Articles for other publications, poems, serial stories, reviews were among the ideas he had in mind. And not the least of these was a book, which he decided to call "The Paris Sketch Book." It was to be based on his experiences and reactions as correspondent in the city on the Seine, and he was at present collecting notes, recording impressions and odd bits of material as he went along.

One idea, he discovered, led to another. As he delved into the history of Paris, studying the types of society, he dreamed of writing the story of some continental wanderer, a "gentleman" who made his living in the gambling halls of Europe, a man who would tell his black history without once forgetting politeness or fine manners. It would be a work of supreme irony throughout. William had even thought of a name for this "hero": Barry Lyndon.

In the meantime, there was the regular work to be done, and efforts made to increase the circulation of "The Constitutional."

"With the Paris column, we should be able to interest a number of subscribers here," he said to Isabella. "And my father says they are having a subscription drive at home."

But though the circulation increased slightly, the paper did not offer much profit, and by March of 1837 William had to give up his post in Paris for lack of funds to pay his salary. He and Isabella returned to London, moving into the house at 18 Albion Street with his parents. He jumped in as a man of all work in a mighty effort to put the paper on its feet. He and the Major worked night and day with the small staff, William pursuing his task with a kind of fury, for he had a special reason. Isabella and he were soon to be mother and father. It was strange to imagine himself a father, as he did in odd moments, but he had little time for imaginings of any sort outside his work. The paper must be on its feet financially by the time the baby arrived.

But in spite of all their efforts, "The Constitutional" showed small sign of improvement. It simply did not "catch on." Subscriptions began to dwindle rather than increase. On June 9, 1837, little Anne Isabella (named for William's mother and wife) came into the world, and three weeks later, on July 1, the last issue of "The Constitutional" was published. The shareholders refused to advance any more money, and the Major, who had already lost a good deal in the enterprise, decided to move to Paris, where he and Mrs. Carmichael-Smyth could live modestly on the remainder of their income.

William had a family to support and no job. But he had no fear of the future. After the baby was born, his spirits were higher than ever. "I think happiness is better than prayers," he told Isabella, as he watched her powdering the baby after its bath one morning. "Mine will serve as the springboard to security, you'll see."

Isabella, only half-hearing him while she finished tending the baby, nodded serenely. She had perfect confidence in her husband.

"I saw Dr. Maginn, my old associate on the "Standard," the other day," William went on, "and he suggested that I submit articles to "Fraser's." He is one of the regular contributors, and thinks I should have no trouble being accepted."

Isabella came forth with a sudden suggestion: "My Uncle Sterling might be able to secure a place on the 'Times' for you." "Of course, I'll see him at once!" William kissed Isabella, placed a peck on the baby's soft cheek, and was off to see Colonel Sterling, one of the stockholders on the "London Times."

A few days later, the young author, husband and father was busy writing a book review for the "Times" in his new post as critic. He was also preparing a manuscript to submit to "Fraser's," for which he had planned illustrations he would furnish himself.

"I think I shall call myself 'Titmarsh,' not 'Timothy Titmarsh' as I've been doing," he said, referring to the pseudonym he had been using, "but a more fitting first name." He mused a moment, his eyes twinkling. "I have it: Michelangelo Titmarsh!"

"Because you're the artist — oh, William!" Isabella laughed.

"Not only that." William rubbed his flat nose thoughtfully. "Michelangelo had his nose broken, and by a fellow student, Torrigiano. Our background is practically identical, you see."

They laughed together, and then William left her to go into the little room which served as his study, where he went to work on an imaginary diary he had begun, written by an imaginary butler, Jeames Yellowplush. The diary, or "papers" as they were called, were to be a commentary on British society of the day, its snobbishness and foibles as seen through the eyes of an equally snobbish butler.

On August 3, William's review of Mr. Thomas Carlyle's book, "The French Revolution," appeared in the "London Times." William had met Mr. Carlyle at Colonel Sterling's, and found both the writer and his book intriguing. The review, therefore, was provocative, and even controversial.

It caused a great deal of speculation as to the identity of the reviewer. But Carlyle knew. He wrote to a friend:

> The writer is one Thackeray, a half-monstrous, Cornish giant, kind of painter, Cambridge man, and Paris newspaper correspondent, who is now writing for his life in London. I have seen him at Sterling's. His article is rather like him and I suppose calculated to do the book good.

Two months later, in the November 1 issue of "Fraser's," the first of the "Yellowplush" papers appeared. The readers were delighted with Jeames Yellowplush, so called because of his breeches. William took the surname from old John Goldsworthy's mustard-colored attire, and something of the running comment in the column came from the conversation of that valuable servant, who still worked for him. Old John now helped Isabella take care of the baby, in addition to his duties as valet and handyman.

With the success of the first installment, "Fraser's" requested other material besides the "Yellowplush" papers from the promising new author. They would like to see short stories, a novel, anything he wrote.

"We're in, Tobykins, we're in!" William picked up his small wife and whirled around the room with her. "If I can push my gold pen across enough pages, we shan't have to worry again. We're on our way, nothing can stop us!" He whirled faster.

"Wait a minute, William!" Isabella was laughing, but her hand, trembling, went across her eyes. "I feel so dizzy . . ."

"Forgive me, Toby." William set her down. "I'm such an ox." He kept forgetting how frail his wife was, like a wild rose — its beauty seemed sturdy, but one strong wind could scatter the petals to the ground.

Once he had received his start, William's energy knew no bounds. Besides the "Yellowplush Papers," he wrote other columns: the "Fitzboodle Papers," "Dolly Duster" and miscellaneous material came from his pen for every issue. A short story, entitled, "The Great Hoggarty Diamond," was surprisingly successful. Neither he nor the publishers had expected it to be so well received. Nor had he forgotten his hopes for the "Paris Sketch-Book."

"Book publication is the next step," he said to Isabella. He gathered notes once more; he wrote to Fitz and asked if he might use some of his friend's translations of the French poet, Beranger.

"Use them if you choose," was Fitzgerald's prompt reply, and into the sketchbook material went the poems. William felt he must take full advantage of the still small, but growing demand for his work. His family was increasing. They needed a larger house, and early in 1838 moved into a comfortable place at 13 Great Coram Street.

Here William had a room downstairs for his study, quite shut off from the rest of the house, where he would retire after breakfast to work industriously until the midday meal. Then he would go up to take his mutton chop with Isabella, and play with small "Annie," who was just beginning to walk. Sometimes there were interruptions. Today, for example, just when he was well into the opening chapter of a short novel that had recently come to him, there was a soft tapping at his door. Without getting up, or stopping his work, he called, "Come."

The knob turned quietly, and in another moment Isabella stole into the room with Annie on her back, the baby's chubby arms around her neck. What a picture the two made! William longed to take up his drawing pencil and sketch them

on the spot, but any drawing he did must be on his illustrations for the stories in "Fraser's." So, with a little smile
and pretended sternness, he reproached her with: "Isabella,
you're breaking our rules. No interruptions before noon!"

"But Annie wanted her papa," Isabella protested.

"Papa," lisped the baby after her, holding out one dimpled
hand to him and nearly losing her balance.

William had to laugh, and rising, took Annie from her
mother and held her for a few minutes. Then Isabella
carried her back upstairs, and as William settled down to his
work again, he heard the sound of the pianoforte in the
drawing-room. His wife was playing waltzes to keep the little
girl amused. Later, the sound of baby talk and piping laughter came to him dimly as he scribbled on. John Goldsworthy
must be taking Annie for her morning air in the garden,
William thought in the back of his mind, and Isabella had
probably gone to lie down before luncheon.

The novel, "Catherine," the first installment of which
"Fraser's" published in May of 1838, caused a good bit of
controversy as it went along. It was a realistic story which
William wrote to show up the false heroism certain novels of
the day were giving to the lives of highwaymen and burglars.
He sought to reveal the ugliness of their crimes in all their
villainy, and many readers found his picture revolting. However, it was honest, it set people talking, and the publishers
were pleased. A writer who could hold public interest must
be encouraged. "Fraser's" wished to print more fiction by
"Michelangelo Titmarsh."

Of course, he would do another story for them. He sometimes felt he would write anything for anybody if it meant

security for his family. He even secretly considered the reactionary papers as a possible market. The pay — and the number of them — was by far the greatest in England. Certainly, it was attractive . . .

He was relieved when word came one day that he had been put up for the Reform Club, an organization composed of broad-minded writers and thinkers. He did not have the twenty guineas to spare for the dues, but he did not withdraw from the membership.

"This will bring me into cohesion with Liberal men, and keep me out of the temptation to write for Tory papers," he said in a letter to his parents. Men like Dickens belonged to the Reform Club. In the presence of such figures, he, William, would not have the face to sell his work to any but liberal magazines like "Fraser's."

He began a new novel for them. "A Shabby Genteel Story," he called it, a pathetic, gently ironic story of a shabby hero (who considered himself a "gentleman") and the innocent girl who fell in love with him. The manuscript for "The Paris Sketchbook" was taking on its final form, and the idea of Barry Lyndon hovered close to the surface of William's active pen, demanding expression.

He was working hard, taking little time for recreation. In the evening a friend might drop in for a smoke and a chat. Sometimes it was Jackie Kemble, who was on the "British and Foreign Review" staff, and had been put up for the post of Examiner of Plays. Sometimes it was Macready, or one of the Fraserians, as the contributors to the magazine called themselves.

Once a month, the Fraserians had dinner together in the publisher's office in Paternoster Row, above the bookstalls. Here William "talked shop" with his colleagues: what the new books and publications were, the latest markets, top rates and the critics to seek out for "puffs" on one's work.

"There is a scarcity of literary talk at our meetings," he told Isabella humorously, "but plenty of practical information on the best way to earn a living as an author. I heard only tonight of a publisher who may be interested in the 'Paris Sketch-Book.' MaCrone is the name — a minor house but a good one, they say. Toby, I believe we're beginning to see our goal."

But his beloved Toby was too sleepy to do more than nod. She was tired a great deal of the time these days. She seemed to live in some remote world of her own, regarding her household of two small daughters, her husband, and old John as if from a vast distance. Then one day, like the wild rose he had compared her to, William's lovely wife, suffering in mind rather than body, suddenly went to pieces.

It was just after publication of the "Paris Sketch-Book," which came out in July, 1840. William was anxious for its success. He wrote to one critic, "Give poor Titmarsh a puff, for certainly no man ever wanted one more than he." He sent letters to several other reviewers, asking for favorable notices. He did not care what these men thought of his pleas. His pride was swept away by the industrious broom of his career: he must be noticed, he must make good financially for the sake of his wife and children.

"The Spectator" carried the best review of "The Paris Sketch-Book." It called his sketches "masterly, and distinguished by grotesque drollery, of a caustic kind that is shown to advantage in hitting off the expressions of villains and dupes." There were others, not quite as enthusiastic, but favorable. Henry Chorley, of the "Athenaeum," was more than generous. William received eight or nine puffs in all, and in gratitude and relief he sent thank you notes to the critics who praised him.

Momentarily exhausted, he went over to the continent for a few days' relaxation with his mother and the Major. He returned greatly refreshed, ready for work once more, eager to share his plans for the future with Isabella.

But his wife hardly greeted him. She spoke listlessly, with a hopeless, vacant stare in her eyes. She sat huddled in her chair, drooping, the freshness he loved so well utterly gone from her. It was as if a blight had struck the wild rose.

William knelt beside her, trying to bring back the spirit that had always charmed him — the tinkling laugh, the sweet, trilling voice. Isabella was tired, he told himself. He would take her away, he would engage the best doctors to cure her. But though he was to go on for several years trying unsuccessfully to help her, outwardly refusing to believe till the last that she would never again be mentally well, he felt in his heart even at this moment that Isabella was lost to him.

He must climb the rest of the way alone.

28

Up the Steep Pathway

ONE OF THE MANY JOURNEYS William and Isabella made in search of her health was to Ireland. Her mother had moved back to the Shawes' home, and William was hopeful that the sight of old surroundings might restore his wife's spirits. And to pay for the expense of this travel, perhaps he could write a book on the order of the one he had just published. He would follow the pattern even in the title, which was to be "The Irish Sketch-Book."

The sojourn was not successful, for Mrs. Shawe, with her irascible temper and scolding tongue, only made matters worse. But William, once the idea of the sketch book had taken form and been tentatively accepted by the publishers, was determined to go through with it. After removing Isabella from the influence of her mother, and putting her under the care of a specialist, he made an extended tour of Ireland, jotting down notes for his book along the way.

When he returned, the house at 13 Great Coram Street seemed unbearably lonely. He had left the little girls in Paris with their grandmother and G.P., as Annie called the Major (short for grandpapa). William, alone with his memories, found it too quiet now to write. He felt the need of old friends, and went to visit Monckton Milnes at the family estate in Yorkville for a few weeks. When he came back, he still felt he must have company, and sent word to Fitz, who came to London at once.

"Do you need financial help?" his loyal comrade wanted to

know. "I know your expenses must be high. I can spare a little . . . "

"No, no. I want only your good companionship," William assured him. He smiled. "Once we begin to talk, I shall feel I'm being idle, and that you are keeping me from my work. Then perhaps I shall get at it."

So the two talked, and smoked their pipes, as they had done many times before, Fitz dreamy and philosophic, Thack curious, restless, and intense in a quiet sort of way.

"You were right about my expenses," he confessed one evening. "They are high. But it's my job to take care of them myself, and somehow it's a challenge to me. I keep thinking up ways and means. I heard the other night that Bradbury and Evans are going to start a new magazine to be called "Punch." It will carry all sorts of comic pieces — political cartoons and satire. I believe I'll offer my services to them. What do you say?"

But for once his friend did not urge him into a new field. "If I were you I should wait till the magazine is well established," was his opinion. "It may fail, and you would be out your labor."

They turned to other subjects. Like David and Jonathan, they could discuss all manner of things as kindred spirits. They suffered each other's cares, and sought to lessen such woes with the understanding that lies in lasting friendship. It was with regret that William saw Edward go back to Boulge cottage, but he knew if Fitz stayed much longer "The Irish Sketch-Book" would never be completed. His life would be lonely, but if he kept busy enough, perhaps he wouldn't mind it.

Then another old friend came back into his life. Willy Brookfield, the dashing figure of Cambridge days, who had since gone into the clergy, moved into a house across the street from William's, bringing with him his bride, the lovely Jane Octavia Brookfield. It was a raw January day in 1842 when William went to call on his new neighbors, and found a source of comfort.

Mrs. Brookfield, a dark, olive-skinned beauty with thoughtful blue eyes, received him with gracious ease. "I'm glad you called so soon," she told him. "You see us at our worst, and that is the best way to be neighborly." Her husband had asked William to stay for dinner, and though she hurriedly sent out for tarts, she was afraid the dessert seemed skimpy.

But William in turn set her at her ease. "I'll just take a two-penny one," he said when the plate was offered.

Everyone laughed. They were friends. Great Coram Street assumed a different air; it was home once more. Nearly every day William made his way across the road, or the Brookfields came to his house. They had discussions, musical evenings, tea or dinner together. They met, too, at the homes of mutual acquaintances, for they had many in common.

William was able to work once more, and went at his task with a will. "The Irish Sketch-Book" was nearing completion, and he had begun at last to outline the story of Barry Lyndon. In spite of the way Fitz had cautioned him against becoming involved with an untried publication, he sent a manuscript to "Punch" which was accepted with a request for more.

Surprisingly enough, this new periodical caught on almost at once. It was loaded with wit and sparkling humor, a spicy addition to the publications of the day. William wished to meet the staff of "Punch" as soon as the first issue was out. Douglas Jerrold, who had been on "The Constitutional," was one of the editors on hand to greet him the day he visited the editorial offices. And who was the tall young man coming toward them, his hand outstretched?

"Thack — good old Thack, don't you remember me?"

William had noticed the name of the artist who had drawn Mr. Punch himself, and wondered about it. Now he knew it could be none other than his one-time schoolmate. "John Leech!" He took the younger man's hand. "I hoped when I saw the name of Mr. Punch's creator that it would be you. Congratulations, John. You have become a true caricaturist."

"Thank you." John was flustered by such praise. "But what about you? What are you doing now?"

"Writing. A little illustrating." William smiled.

"You are? In what papers?"

William, adjusting his monocle, drawled casually, "Oh, 'Fraser's,' 'Punch.' "

" 'Punch'? Under what name?"

"Michelangelo Titmarsh, at your service." William bowed.

"So you're Titmarsh! Why, I have been reading your work for several years now, and I never dreamed — " John broke off and shook his head, marvelling. Then he asked, "Why don't you use your real name, Thack?"

"I'm not sure enough of myself yet," William admitted. "A pen name is like protective armor. Titmarsh may be attacked, but William Thackeray remains intact. I don't want to expose him till I'm dead sure he will be safe."

Nevertheless, when "The Irish Sketch-Book" came out, he drew aside his protective armor in the dedication, when he signed his name to the closing words: "Laying aside for a moment the travelling title of Mr. Titmarsh, let me acknowledge these favors in my own name, and subscribe myself, W. M. Thackeray."

After this quick show of face, however, he hid in his shell

once more. "Barry Lyndon," which "Fraser's" began to publish in installments, was signed by Titmarsh; and "The Snob
Papers," his first efforts for "Punch," used this pseudonym.

"The Snob Papers," or "Book of Snobs," as William first
titled them, were exaggerated and sometimes vicious portraits of London's fashionables, which proved to be quite
popular. So were "The Ballads of Policeman X," which he
enjoyed writing for the new magazine. John Leech, always
William's admirer, delighted in revealing the true identity
of his friend around Town.

The men at the Garrick Club, the Reform Club, the guests
at fashionable dinner parties began to call William, "Titmarsh." Nearly everyone in literary circles knew who he
was by this time, 1844. But his work was not yet big enough,
he felt. "Barry Lyndon," which was receiving recognition,
was the best so far, but he wanted to wait till he had produced a book on the grand scale before using his real name
alone. He had ideas for a new novel . . .

But before he could formulate his thoughts, he received
the chance to write another travel book. He was offered the
job of journeying to Turkey and Egypt as correspondent for
"Fraser's." Later a book was to be published from his
articles, called, "Notes of a Journey from Cornhill to Grand
Cairo."

"What do you say? Shall I go?" he asked the Brookfields
on the day he received this offer. "I have only forty-eight
hours to get ready." He had come over to consult them, and
Mrs. Brookfield made him accept a cup of tea to calm himself. He took a few sips, set the cup on the table, and began
pacing back and forth in front of the sofa where the Brookfields were sitting. "It means I shall have to interrupt my
other work," he said. "But the pay is good, and I need it.
The doctor's bills for Isabella have been so high, and I send

my parents money for the children — " He spread his hands wide. "I guess I have no choice! Good-bye, Jane. Good-bye, Willy. Thanks for your advice."

And with their laughter behind him, he hurried across the street to pack.

Some months after he returned, in February, 1845, he started on his new novel, the one he had half-conceived before he left. It was a strange sort of novel; there was no hero, and the closest approach to a heroine was a villainess who was its central figure. It was an outgrowth of "The Book of Snobs," and William called it "Pen and Pencil Sketches of English Society," for he was illustrating the manuscript, as usual. At first the publishers he knew shied away from this, the most outspoken of Titmarsh's writings so far. None of them cared to take a chance on the public reaction to such a work. But finally Bradbury and Evans, who had succeeded in their venture with "Punch," decided to put the book out in installments.

When he returned from Egypt, William had taken his wife from the sanitarium and placed her under the care of Mrs. Bakewell, an old family friend and nurse who lived in Camberwell. The doctors and specialists had done Isabella no good, and it was now plain that she would never be normal. Yet she would be well tended by the nurse and William could visit her here in England occasionally. He suddenly decided, too, that it was time for his little daughters to live with him in London. He had been seeing them only in lightning trips to Paris now and then, and felt that they did not look on him as their father, but more as an amusing, jolly relative who sometimes came to visit. So he bought a new house at 13 Young Street, prepared the nursery and schoolroom, engaged a governess, and wrote his mother to bring the girls home.

What a reunion there was! Annie and Minny, nine and six years old respectively, were overjoyed to be in London with "papa."

"Will you take us to the theater?" Annie wished to find out at once. She knew her father loved the stage, and with her grandparents the girls had led such a quiet life; they rarely went anywhere.

"Will you take us to see the clowns?" asked small Minny.

William hugged them both. "How you have grown up! Yes, we shall go many places together, but you must promise not to disturb me when I am working, or we shall have no money to go anywhere."

The girls promised, and during the hours William wrote they kept away from his study. But when he was not there, or before he started to write, they loved to creep in and examine the array of tools on his desk. He kept a pair of sharp scissors, for one thing, to cut the nibs of his quill pens at a certain angle. And a sharp knife, for his row of pencils. The pencils were the children's chief admiration: they were so evenly cut, so finely pointed.

"When I am a grown lady," Annie decided, "I shall be a writer, and have a row — or maybe two — of sharpened pencils on my desk."

It was just after breakfast. William had risen early to get in an hour's work before the meal, and the girls had come to fetch him when they were dressed. Their tea, muffins and jam consumed, they had begged for a peek in the study before going upstairs for lessons. But they had been here long enough; it was time to shoo them out.

"I hope you will be a writer some day, Annie, but without study you won't be able to string six words together properly — so off with you, my chicks!" William mustered them out of the room. "I will see you later on."

"Are you going to be home for dinner, papa?" Annie asked, for their father dined out several nights a week.

William pulled one of her pigtails gently. "I'm sorry, tonight it's a dinner-party at Mrs. Elliot's. But tomorrow I shall be free, and perhaps we can go to Astley's."

With this bright prospect before them, the girls danced up to their schoolroom, and William settled down to his labors on the current installment of the "Pen and Pencil Sketches."

Mrs. Elliot and her sister, Kate Perry, two elderly women who lived at 18 Chesham Place, were noted for their hospitality, and in their home some of the best minds in London met frequently at dinner. Their father, James Perry, had been editor of "The Morning Chronicle," and his daughters when very young had been charming hostesses to the literary figures the editor wished to entertain. Now Kate Perry, and her widowed sister, Mrs. Elliot, carried on proudly. Tonight William was to find among the guests the Brookfields; Procters; the author, Kinglake; poet, Alfred Tennyson; Monckton Milnes (who had become Lord Houghton) and other famous people.

The sisters were especially fond of William, whom they had come to know well in the year or two since they had been introduced to him, for he appreciated their invitations, rarely turning down the opportunity of going to their home. Both women, particularly Kate Perry, were interested in William's career, and helped to promote it whenever they could.

When, nearly a year later, the "Pen and Pencil Sketches" were close to completion, and had to be put in shape for publication in book form, these kindly sisters invited William to come to their place in Brighton, where he could work undisturbed, and have the benefit of the sea air. He accepted the invitation, leaving the girls in London with their governess.

He had been going at such a pace it was a relief to be at the seaside resort, watching the happy vacationers and breathing the fresh, salt air. His sketches were shaping up nicely, but he needed a title for them if they were going to have any appeal in book form. "Pen and Pencil Sketches of English Society" sounded like a group of essays.

But what was the title to be? All day long he thought about it, and by the time he retired he still had not found a suitable name for his book. He could not sleep. He lay tossing restlessly on his bed in the middle of the night, racking his brains.

This was his first big work — it had feeling, meaning, impact — and he felt, or hoped, it was one to which he could sign his own name for the first time. William pondered, as he turned wakefully from side to side, the strange diffidence that had made him hide his identity for so long. True, a great many authors used pen names throughout their lives. but the custom had been abandoned by most men of letters once they were established. Charles Dickens, who had started out as "Boz," had long since become a household name. Who in England did not know Oliver Twist as synonymous with Dickens? Why, the little man was as well known as Shakespeare! Not that he didn't deserve to be one of England's foremost figures: he worked like a beaver, and his portraits of human nature were startling studies in black and white. How good his heroes were — Nicholas Nickleby, Pickwick, and little Oliver! And how bad his villains, like Fagin.

What was his opinion of the central figure in William's "Pen and Pencil Sketches," Becky Sharpe, who was not at all good, but quite bad? So far Dickens had said nothing about it when the two authors met at Garrick Club meetings. Yet Becky was more the heroine of the story than her friend, Amelia, who epitomized virtue but had no brains, in contrast to Becky's razor-edge intelligence. William had found himself so interested in Becky as a person that he had unconsciously endowed her with the qualities of a heroine. She had spirit, she had moments of genuine feeling in spite of her continual posing, she had charm to spare. Though she did not succeed in her most daring enterprise, she would end her days in financial security, if in social obscurity. She would be a prank, an immortal joke on society, an exposé of its weaknesses, its shabbiness, its underside so skillfully hidden by gilded coverings.

These sketches of English society, now that they were to be bound together, must have a strong, significant, epigrammatic sort of title, especially since the book was to come out under his own name at last. He smiled at his vanity. He was always unsure of himself, uncertain of the value of his work, but he wanted his name to be esteemed by the world once it became known. Yes, he was vain, as most men were — *vanitas vanitatum*.

He fell to thinking of Christian and Faithful, as they came to the town of Vanity in "Pilgrim's Progress," passing through the fair established by Beelzebub, Apollyon and Legion for the sale of vanities: houses, lands, trades, honors, titles, kingdoms, all sorts of pleasures and delights. A fair that lasted all the year round, it was denounced by Christian and Faithful, as William had tried to denounce the vain strivings and machinations of English society. Suddenly he sat bolt upright: he had found a title.

"Vanity Fair! Vanity Fair!" He jumped out of bed, shouting. It was too good to be true — exactly what he had been searching for. "Vanity Fair!" he repeated, running around the room in gleeful excitement. Three times he ran around it, shouting to the walls, "Vanity Fair, Vanity Fair!" In all his career, he had never felt so triumphant.

Once it was published in the summer of 1848, however, the book was slow to gain recognition from the public. Only in literary circles was the work appreciated, and then opinion on it was varied. Fitz sent a note complimenting him on it, but William felt he was merely being kind.

"I daresay I let my hopes soar too high," he said disconsolately to the Brookfields one evening. " 'Vanity Fair' was probably unworthy of public acclaim, anyhow."

Mrs. Brookfield smiled at him above her embroidery hoop. "The only trouble with your book is that it has too much merit. It will take time for the general public to appreciate your writing. Once they do, you'll receive acclaim, never fear! Only you must be patient."

"You are a great comfort," William thanked her. "Unfortunately, my creditors are not patient," he fumed a moment later. "I can't eat my words, you know!"

But though he might clown with his friends, William was quite downcast at the lagging interest shown in his novel since its publication in book form. Success was still a long way off, it seemed.

Then a singular thing happened. Charlotte Brontë, whose book had been the rage of England almost from its publication date, dedicated the second edition of "Jane Eyre" to "that little known master of English literature, William Makepeace Thackeray."

"I cannot believe it!" William was astonished, but delighted as he read and re-read the glowing tribute Miss Brontë paid to his writing in general, and to "Vanity Fair" in particular. "Imagine the author of 'Jane Eyre' knowing and praising my work to this extent!"

He had never met Miss Brontë, though he admired her powers of story-telling: he had sat up all night reading "Jane Eyre," and whatever its faults were, surely no one could deny its powerful development of plot, its tremendous display of emotion. It was a signal honor to have the second edition of such a work inscribed to him. He wrote a letter thanking the extraordinary woman novelist at once, and she quickly answered. It was the beginning of a friendship between the two, by way of a spirited correspondence. Later on, they met through Miss Brontë's publisher, George Smith, and continued the sharp exchange of wit in person.

The "dedication of the second edition" marked the turning point in the fate of "Vanity Fair" as far as general recognition was concerned. Public curiosity had been aroused. Sales of the novel grew steadily. The name of William Makepeace Thackeray was gradually becoming known not only in London but all over England as well. The "great world" of society showered him with attention.

Like most of his old friends, Monckton Milnes had been strong in his support of William's talents from the first, but now the young baronet introduced his Cambridge crony with pride at the London breakfasts for which he was famous, or at his house parties at Fryston, the family estate. "My friend, Thackeray — author of 'Vanity Fair,' you know," he would say casually as he introduced William, and there would be a little stir and rustle of those nearby, who turned to take a second look, or pressed forward to meet the author of that remarkable book.

The silver tray on the hall table at 13 Young Street was kept full of cards and invitations from high-ranking titles of the realm. Most of these William accepted, because, as much as he might criticize society, he loved splendor and cheer, and the feeling of warmth against his loneliness that it gave him to be surrounded by admiration and attention.

Not that he was accepted without protest from the more conventional people. Lord and Lady Stanley of Alderly Park, two of his close friends, recommended "Vanity Fair" to their relatives as soon as they read it. Lady Stanley was a liberal who worked for the education of women. But in 1849 she received an acid note from her mother-in-law: "I have read 'Vanity Fair,' and how anybody can like to associate with the author astonishes me — though I daresay his conversation may not be like his book exactly, but I should so dislike the man who could give such a work to the public." Later there was a second: "How can you tolerate Thackeray for showing you all up in the manner he does. . . . Really, he should be banished from the society he has so wonderfully found his way into, only to hold it up to ridicule."

But he was not banished, only asked more and more, until his colleagues thought surely his head must be turned by such adulation. Thomas Carlyle hinted to Edward Fitzgerald, with whom he corresponded, that "Thackeray had become a tremendous lion." Fitz, who was quick to feel neglect on the part of his intimates, wrote to one of them: "Thackeray goes to Holland House and Devonshire House and for some reason will not write a word to me. But I am sure this is not because he is asked to Holland House," he added, in defense of William's character. Still, Fitz thought, he had received no answer to the note in praise of "Vanity Fair."

Carlyle's remark reached William's ears. Much upset, he wrote to Fitz:

> It is not true what Gurlyle [his nickname for Carlyle] has written to you about my becoming a tremenjous lion etc., too grand to etc.; but what is true is that a fellow who is writing all day for money gets sick of pen and paper when his work is over, and I go on dawdling and thinking of writing (to you) and months pass away. All that about my being a lion is nonsense. "Vanity Fair" does everything but pay. I am glad if you like it. I don't care a dem if some other people do or don't, and always try to keep that damper against flattery.

He posted the letter at once.

He ardently hoped he had not insulted dear old Fitz, of all people. There was one man who had no vanity, nothing vainglorious in his nature; he was genuine down to the finest fiber. No success, no amount of acclaim was worth the loss of a crony like Fitz. William wished suddenly that he might see his old friend just at this time when his head was spinning from the commotion of growing fame.

It was nearly a year before the two met, when Fitz came to London on one of his rare excursions. William in the meantime had nearly completed a new novel.

Partly to get away from the tumult that followed "Vanity Fair," and partly because an idea had begun to take shape in his mind, William took Annie and Minny on a trip to Devonshire, to visit his old home, Larkbeare. The house was still there, square and comfortable-looking. Ottery Hall had been repaired; there were tenants in the manor house now. The little village of Ottery St. Mary had remained unchanged, though most of the people he remembered were gone. Dr. Cornish had died, and there was a new vicar in the church.

The girls loved walking into the past with their father. What a quaint country village and cozy inn where they stayed overnight! Annie and Minny whispered to each other in low tones before they went to sleep. Papa had jotted down notes all day as they wandered over the old, familiar paths. He had made sketches, hasty maps showing landmarks, and he set down quickly, eagerly, information picked up at random from the villagers. He must be planning to write a new book about Larkbeare.

And so he was. In the morning he was in high spirits over his prospects for a novel, its opening scenes to be set in his former surroundings, its hero a young man whose fortunes were to bear a marked resemblance to William Thackeray's.

"My work is nearly done here," he said to the girls as he met them outside their door, and the three descended the steep narrow stair to the lower floor of the inn where travellers were being served the morning meal, "but before we go, we must have a Devonshire breakfast." He ordered some dark bread, gooseberry jam, and heavy, sweet cream to go with it.

"This is what I used to eat when I was a boy," he told the girls. The taste of the bread and jam with Devonshire cream carried the flavor of the past, and as they sat by the open inn door eating their breakfast and breathing the sweet, country air, William described the scenes of his boyhood for his young daughters. He told them how he used to come home half-frozen from Charterhouse in the winter, of the adventures he had riding his little mare, Rachel, and of the way he and Mary Graham — Polly — (who was now married to the Major's younger brother, Colonel Carmichael) had been like brother and sister during the days at Larkbeare.

The heroine of his new novel, who was to be called Laura, would be much like his cousin as he remembered her twenty years before. And his mother would be in the novel, as Helen Pendennis, the mother of Arthur Pendennis, the "hero." Once again he was going to create a leading character who was not heroic at all, but a rather weak, vain, naïve boy, charming in a way, but laughable, and sometimes pathetically simple. Pendennis was to represent the reckless, carefree, unstable side of William's nature. He would even be a "little fellow" physically. His friend, Warrington, great of stature, rugged of face, was to represent the dark, melancholy, cynical side of William's nature and whatever strength he might possess. He had always felt himself to be two people — one who longed for society, the other who shunned and despised it — and by inventing two contrasting characters, he could paint a complete picture of his emotions and experiences as a young man.

The novel, which he called "Pendennis," progressed rapidly once he began writing. William was laughing at his youth in this book, and sympathizing with it as well. In "Vanity Fair," he had depicted his early days at Charterhouse, which he called "Slaughterhouse." "Pendennis" contained scenes at the milder "Greyfriars," built on those last days at Charterhouse, and the change that seemed to come over it when he went back the first time with the Major. Most of William's heroes went to "Greyfriars," for his school years were indelibly engraved in his mind and must become part of his stories. Pendennis went to "Oxbridge" (a combination of Cambridge and Oxford), and to law school; and though his actual history differed from William's, the events of his life took place in the same settings.

Annie and Minny followed the installments of "Pendennis" each month with great interest. They enjoyed their father's writing, though Minny once said to William frankly, "I like Mr. Dickens' stories better than yours, papa." (Her father had laughed, and thought to himself privately that Mr. Dickens probably wrote better stories than he.) Both girls were deeply concerned when Mrs. Pendennis became desperately ill.

"Is she going to die?" Annie had to find out.

"I'm afraid so," William admitted.

"Oh, don't let her die!" Annie wailed.

Minny suggested more practically: "Couldn't she be very sick the way she is now, and then take some homeopathic medicine like grandma's, and get well again?"

Mrs. Carmichael-Smyth was interested in homeopathic medicines just then, and her enthusiasm led the girls to believe it could cure any disease. William nearly let out a roar of laughter, but he said seriously, "No, I'm sorry, girls, but Mrs. Pendennis must die. There is no other way to work out the story." And indeed, when it came to actually writing the death scene, he found he was overcome with sadness, tears rolling down his cheeks as he penned the words.

The book was finished in the fall of 1850, and shortly before publication Fitz came to Town to see "old Thack." William, relieved of the burden of his novel, was in the mood for a holiday, so the two were especially merry together. The girls found Fitz the most delightful of their father's friends; they wished he would visit them more often, for while he was there rules were relaxed, and their father was more carefree and gay than they had ever seen him.

As for Fitz, he was satisfied that William had not become, nor was in danger of becoming a "lion." "He is just the same," Edward reported to a mutual friend of theirs. "All the world admires 'Vanity Fair'. The author is courted by Dukes and Duchesses, and wits of both sexes."

Yet he remained just the same. Because of the popularity of "Vanity Fair," the new book sold a great many copies on publication; the reviews were uniformly good; the publishers asked for another manuscript. William wrote a little Christmas Book, entitled "The Kickleburys on the Rhine," which was enjoyed by young and old. He had an idea for his next work, an historical novel set in the preceding century. But he still wavered between confidence and uncertainty, still scouted around for ways and means to increase his livelihood. He was considering the preparation of a series of lectures on the English humorists. However, in spite of his misgivings, he was making rapid strides toward the top.

29

The Goal in Sight

THE LECTURES on the English humorists, which William
delivered during the fall of 1851 at Cambridge, Oxford and
Edinburgh, proved to be a huge success, financially and
otherwise. Those who didn't know the name of Thackeray
before were well acquainted with it now that his big figure,
his over-sized head with curly white hair, and his soft drawl
were familiar to thousands who heard the lectures and went
home discussing them. It was the surprise of William's life
that audiences should so take to his personality.

"I tell you, John, it's amazing," he said to John Leech as
they sat over their cigars at the club on a snowy night following the tour. "Hundreds of faces upturned toward mine,
listening, watching my every gesture — as though I were
Macready!"

"What did you expect?" John was sketching his friend
idly on a club circular. "Empty houses?"

"Well, yes. Or at any rate, boredom, or disgust with my
brand of speech-making. I'm no orator, you know." William
threw one leg over the arm of his chair, and leaned back,
blowing out a great puff of smoke. "Lord, I was frightened
opening night! Don't know what I should have done if it
hadn't been for Fanny Kemble, or Mrs. Butler, I should say.
She married that American."

John nodded. "Did she coach you?"

William shook his head. "Not exactly. She arrived early,
and found me pacing the stage, ready to leave by the nearest
exit. She made me go into the green room to settle down

while the audience was coming in, and I left my notes on the podium. I thought I might feel more confident if I could look them over just before going on, and she went out to fetch them." He laughed. "She must have been more nervous than I, because she dropped the papers! They went scattering across the stage, and of course by the time she retrieved them they were hopelessly mixed up."

"A great help," John put in.

"Oddly enough, it was." There was still surprise in William's voice as he recalled the way he had suddenly grown calm and collected. "I suppose having to sort out those papers straightened the lecture out in my mind as well. At any rate, by the time I finished, I knew exactly what I was going to say, and I was no longer afraid."

"I can testify to your coolness," John said. "I never saw anyone more self-possessed. I should never have suspected your fright."

"Good, I'm glad to hear it. Don't repeat what I've told you to our colleagues, and my reputation is safe." William sighed with satisfaction, and smoked on in silence for several minutes. Then he said slowly, "I want to leave a good impression behind me when I resign from "Punch.""

John looked up from his drawing. "And when is that to be?"

"Right now. I've already written my resignation." William measured his words, waiting for John's reaction.

"No!" John dropped his pencil and let the caricature of William slip to the floor. "But why, Thack?"

"Because I would rather devote myself to books from now on. Between long works and lectures, I have no time for magazine articles. I must concentrate on what brings in the most money, you know."

"I suppose so," John said gloomily. "But 'Punch' won't be

the same. I feel like resigning, too, if you won't be there."

"As the creator of Punch himself, you are indispensable, John. I'm not," William pointed out.

And though his old friend and colleague tried to dissuade him, he resigned from the contributing staff of the magazine shortly afterward. His historical novel, set in Queen Anne's time, demanded research as well as time for writing it. He was anxious to make his book an accurate picture of the times he had chosen. Henry Esmond, his hero, whose name served as the title, must not be guilty of actions unbefitting the early eighteenth century.

William spent the next six months in concentrated work on his manuscript, finishing it on the twenty-eighth of May, 1852. It was a lovely spring day, and to celebrate, he took the girls for a drive, stopping afterwards for dinner.

"Henry Esmond" came out in October, and was a more instantaneous success than either "Vanity Fair" or "Pendennis." It was a fine piece of craftsmanship, told an absorbing story, and possessed characters so alive they seemed to step out of the pages and into the reader's life. As usual, William was leery of the worth of his latest book. He might think it his best work, but was it really good? He could not place a proper value on it; he was still too much a part of it.

He saw, however, that the public appreciated his efforts, buying copies of "Henry Esmond" in great numbers. Quite without knowing it, he had become an accepted, established author.

"Girls," William said to his young daughters one day, "I think I shall go to America. They have asked me to repeat my lecture series over there. What do you say?" He wanted to give the girls the chance to express themselves on the advisability of his going. They were old enough — Annie was fifteen, Minny, twelve — to be consulted occasionally on matters of importance. Although they were by no means beautiful, both were lively and winning in manner, and keenly interested in all that concerned their father.

But at the thought of his going so far away, they were little children again.

"America? But that's thousands of miles from here, papa!" Annie protested. "Do you have to accept?"

"Their offer is very good." William took a letter from his pocket and opened it. "If I speak to full houses — and this letter assures me I will — I shall earn twice as much as I did here."

"Don't go, papa," Minny pleaded. "The boat may sink, and you will be drowned."

William did his best to assure her there was no danger, though the voyage seemed dark and perilous to him, too. But in the interest of his career, he thought he should go, and he finally convinced the girls that the advantages of the tour would make it worthwhile. At the last moment, however, he wrote to Fitz asking his old friend to act as his executor and guardian to the girls if anything should happen to him. Beset by mingled hopes and fears, he embarked at last on the royal mail ship, *Canada,* accompanied by Eyre Crowe, the son of his companions of Paris days, who was to act as his secretary. When the ship pulled away from the dock, William longed to turn it back, and he wondered whether he would ever see the shores of England again.

His fear dissolved, however, as soon as they were well at sea. There were notables on board, among them James Russell Lowell, who proved diverting throughout the voyage. And America, big, friendly, sprawling, young, active America, had the atmosphere of a carnival about it — colorful, laughing, bustling with enterprise. How busy, how eager and ambitious the people were!

W. M. T. on his travels

They were warmhearted, too. William and his young companion found themselves feted on their first night in Boston with an oyster supper at the Tremont House. There were dinners, too, at one of which the two travellers received their first taste of turkey. (Eyre Crowe, who was keeping a record of the journey, made particular note of this new fowl which neither had ever encountered before.) There were long, quiet talks with the literary men of Boston: Hawthorne; George Ticknor, the Spanish historian; Lowell, and many others.

The novels of William Thackeray were extremely popular in America, but they brought no revenue to the author because they were "pirated" by American publishers, just as English publishers pirated the works of Hawthorne, Irving and Poe. Copyright laws were not yet established. His popularity, however, brought large audiences to William's lectures in Boston, paving the way for further success in New York.

As he sat waiting for a train in the Boston station, a rosy-cheeked boy selling books came by, calling: "Thackeray's works, Thackeray's works!" William, amazed to find his books being sold in an American railway station, stopped the little salesman.

"Thackeray's works, sir?" asked the boy.

"Which ones have you?" William rummaged among the assortment in the basket, and was astonished to find a copy of "A Shabby Genteel Story." He had not seen one in years. He bought the book, and re-read it during the ride to New York. Though it had many faults which he could see clearly now, he became absorbed in the story, and wished he had not brought it to such a hurried close. Perhaps he could write a sequel to it, or a novel that might concern itself with other characters, but would take up where this left off . . .

New York was a pageant of color and action. Broadway was alive with brisk sleighs of different sizes, shapes, and hues, whose bells rang out gaily over the snow-covered streets. There were even sleigh-stages, open cars on runners, and the conductor walked around on a "cradle," collecting fares. The metropolis gave promise of even greater harvest than William had reaped from his lectures in Boston, and indeed, the speeches at the Unitarian Church here were given before packed audiences. He had to double the number.

In New York, he met Horace Greeley, the famous newspaper man, who helped William out on the maze of American politics; Washington Irving, "Old Knick," the lion of New York, with whom the British author had a quiet gossip at the Clarendon; and James Harper of Harper Brothers, who introduced William to his little girl. Taking her hand, William said, "So this is a pirate's daughter, is it?"

He was introduced to a great many people in New York, but of them all, he enjoyed the Baxter family the most. Mother, father, and three lovely daughters, friendly, kind and understanding, he came to love them all before his return to England. They invited him to dinner before one of the lectures, and after that first engagement, he went back again and again until the brownstone front house in which the Baxters lived was another home to him. If he had gained nothing else, the friendship he formed with this delightful family would make the trip to America worthwhile.

William's next appearances were in Washington, and the stay in the capital was a succession of balls, concerts, parties and banquets, until he scarcely had energy enough left for the lectures. He managed to complete the course, however, and at one engagement at Carusi's Rooms, he was honored by the presence of both President Fillmore, just finishing his term, and President Pierce, newly elected in November.

Down the Potomac to Richmond the two travellers went next, and from there to Charleston, and south to Savannah. where they were bitten by fleas till they could not sleep. The name of the British author was not as well known here as in the north, and although the price of the lectures, one dollar for two, was less than it had been there, the series was not as well attended. William was all at once weary of journeying up and down a strange country, facing a sea of people at each new place. When he and Eyre Crowe arrived in New York again, the two stayed only long enough for

William to visit the Baxters, and then left suddenly, one spring morning, sailing at a moment's notice — to be in England when April was there.

Writing, writing, writing, writing. It was the keynote of William's life once he had become an established, and indeed, a celebrated novelist, known as he was on two continents. Public and publishers alike clamored for more books. "The Newcomes," his next long work, was written in large part during a holiday tour he took with Annie and Minny in Europe after his return from America. The idea for a story about a big family, the Newcomes, one of whom — Colonel Newcome — was to be a combination of the Major and Richmond Shakespear, had come to him out of nowhere. As the plot spread before him in his mind, like a flower opening in water, he must set it down on paper, whether he was in Switzerland, France or Rome, the last stop on the tour. In Rome, Annie and Minny were taken ill with scarlatina, and to amuse them, their father began a fairy tale, providing a new installment each day of a delightful fantasy called, "The Rose and the Ring." It was brought out as a Christmas Book by Smith, Elder and Company, William's new publishers, in December, 1854. "The Newcomes" appeared shortly afterward.

This long novel was linked to "Pendennis" by means of having Pendennis edit the story of the Newcomes, as well as having some of the characters of the earlier book enter into the plot. William hated to see the people about whom he wrote, his own creations, fade away completely once a book was published. Into the new novel, therefore, came Pendennis and Laura, and Captain Costigan, a red-nosed rascal loved by all those who had read "Pendennis." William planned to connect all his writings by mentioning his characters in more than one book, or having the central figure in one play a lesser part in another. In this way, his readers would feel they were meeting old friends in every work, and come to watch for familiar names. His next manuscript, another historical novel, called "The Virginians," was to be a sequel to "Henry Esmond."

The new publishers proved to be much more generous in their terms than Fraser's. William moved his family to a larger house at 36 Onslow Square, and rented a summer place, Chateau Brequereque, at Boulogne, where he and the girls spent three months with his mother and the Major after "The Newcomes" was finished.

Mrs. Carmichael-Smyth took great pride in her son's career. The two had long talks about his books and his plans for those to come. Young Annie started to work as her father's secretary, taking down the paragraphs as he dictated them. He walked to and fro while he thought, puffing on his inevitable cigar.

In the privacy of her room, after her secretarial duties were done, Annie worked on a novel of her own. She had been writing poems and short stories for several years, and now she wanted to try something more ambitious. She would never be a famous author like her father, but she could not help writing.

William had praised and encouraged her childish attempts, but he was too busy at present to inquire into her latest efforts. He was preparing a new set of lectures on the four King Georges who had ruled England. The household at Chateau Brequereque was an extremely busy one from June to September.

The lectures on the four Georges were so successful that William received another invitation to America. He accepted, but the second tour was not as satisfying as the first. Americans were not as interested in British kings as Englishmen were. The humorists had had much more appeal in the United States. William scarcely saw the Baxters; he was ill several times in the course of the tour; and the travel seemed much more inconvenient. He was glad when it was time to go home.

He began work on "The Virginians" at once, plotting its story as a continuation of "Henry Esmond," according to his plan. Only this one would be concerned with Henry Esmond's grandsons. Writing, writing, writing, writing. . . .

Before he was quite finished with "The Virginians," George Smith, the president of Smith, Elder and Company, called on him unexpectedly one morning. He was a slender young man, who dressed like a dandy and was always brimful of new ideas.

He wasted no time this morning in taking a prospectus from his frockcoat. "I have a proposition for you, Thackeray," he announced. "How would you like to be the editor of a new magazine Smith, Elder and Company are going to publish?" He placed the papers on the writing table.

William picked them up slowly. "It is a temptation, Smith, but suppose I have lost the energy an editorship requires? I don't know whether I could read manuscripts of others in addition to writing my own. And then I have such a difficult time rejecting anybody's work. I know what a struggle it is to write. I should always be wanting to help some poor devil out, no matter what sort of flam he sent us. — By the way," he pulled his trouser pockets inside out, "can you lend this poor devil a helping hand?"

George Smith, who took care of William's finances, pulled out his checkbook. "How much?"

"A hundred pounds," William said.

The publisher nodded, scribbled the figures, and handed him the check. "Let's say this is an advance on the first installment of a serial to run in the new magazine. We want your name, Thack. We shan't ask too much of you as an editor. You will have assistants. But we would like to have a novel of yours running all the time."

William could not resist his publisher's persuasive manner, and in the end consented to become editor of the magazine, which, after much discussion, was called "Cornhill Magazine." The name was taken from that of the street where most magazines were published. For the first issue, he wrote a column entitled, "The Roundabout Papers," in addition to the first installment of a new novel, "Lovel The Widower." "The Roundabout Papers" were leisurely remembrances of William's youth, true incidents at Charterhouse, his life at Weimar, — all the little incidents he thought the readers might find amusing and interesting.

"The Cornhill Magazine" prospered from the beginning, and William could not help comparing its rapid rise with the sad fate of "The National Standard" and "The Constitutional" in the early days of his career. What a difference it made when your name was well known! He thought of the volume of verse old Fitz had had published the year before, in 1859. It was called "The Rubaiyat of Omar Khayyam," and Edward, with his usual self-effacement, would not sign his name to the translation of the Persian quatrains, on which he had worked several years. Though they were exquisite, melodic, and indeed, original renditions of the Persian poet, they had received scarcely any notice, and were soon consigned to the penny box at the print-sellers'. William wondered whether they would ever be recognized. Fitz did not seem to mind, one way or another: he had only himself to support, and his mother had recently left him moderately well off. He did not feel the urge to keep pushing, striving for the top with the same intensity William did, even though now he was near it.

The editorship, however, was more wearing than he had

expected. For all his energy and desire to guide the "Cornhill Magazine," he found it exhausting to select material, plan issues, and, most of all, to turn down needy authors. Sometimes he accepted, and paid for, manuscripts which were never used, to help the writer. Two years after the first issue came out, he resigned the post of editor, but kept on as contributor. He started a new novel, "Phillip," which began where "A Shabby Genteel Story" had ended, but dealt with the son of the main character in the earlier novel. Pendennis told this story, too, as he had told "The Newcomes," and the Newcome family were to be mentioned in the text somewhere, to give the effect of a social circle where everyone knew everyone else.

Things were going well. George Smith was a liberal publisher, so that William's source of income was never lacking. He bought another home, the largest so far, at 2 Palace Green; "the reddest house in England," he called it, because of its bricks. Amy Crowe, the youngest of the Crowes' daughters, had come to live with the Thackerays, and they did not find the extra room too much for them. Besides, William had always wanted a home where he could entertain properly, to return the many invitations he had accepted from others.

Annie was delighted with the house, which looked out on green trees from all the windows. Shortly after they moved, she brought her father the manuscript she had been working on for so long. She had called her novel, "Elizabeth."

"I don't know what you are going to think of my first book, papa"; she laid it before him on the table; "but I wish you would read it."

William glanced at the bulky manuscript. "When did you write all this, Annie? I have been keeping you so busy."

"I've been working at night, mostly," Annie confessed.

"I should have found another secretary when Eyre Crowe left," William said regretfully. "You need more time to write."

"Indeed? Do you think I would let anyone else have the privilege of setting down your words?" Annie hugged him.

"Never mind the flattery," her father told her. "I'll read your manuscript tonight, and give you my opinion on it."

He sat up most of the night, reading, making marginal notes for Annie's benefit. He was extremely proud of the effort his daughter had made: she had written a good novel, he felt, and without help from him until this moment.

He had little trouble securing a publisher for "Elizabeth," and waited eagerly for the reviews. Most of them were good, and the book had a fair sale, but the April 25 issue of "The Atheneum," 1862, carried what he considered an unfair attack on Annie's work.

"This is an outrage," he said, shaking the paper as he read. "I'll answer them. I'll show them they daren't print such things!"

Annie tried to calm him, but he wrote a bitter reply to the criticism. He somehow considered it an attack on himself. He had never completely overcome the notion that the world was challenging him. He was earning a great deal of money, putting aside a certain amount regularly in an annuity for Annie and Minny. He had more than regained his losses. He had turned all his misfortunes to good account by using them for fodder to his genius. He had carved a generous niche for himself in the hall of fame. Yet he continued to feel that he must prove his worth, that he must hammer into society the fact that he was a first-rate author and gentleman. He enjoyed life's pleasures to the fullest, but he had never mastered its uncertainties.

His goal was in sight, but he pushed himself on, writing

the "Roundabout Papers," and working on another historical novel, "Denis Duval." He attended as many social functions as he could squeeze into his full calendar. It drew near Christmas, the season he loved best, when, among other festivities, he gathered with a group of cronies at the Reform Club to sing the old ballad, "The Mahogany Tree." It was a moment of cheer and good faith that he always looked forward to with pleasure.

But this year he did not sing with his friends.

On December 23, 1863, in the midst of this swirl and press of activities, he was suddenly stricken with a fatal attack of the urological condition that had been bothering him for some years. He died the following day, on Christmas Eve, at the early middle age of fifty-two and at the height of his career — as if he had cast aside his pen without warning, leaving the story of his life dramatically at its zenith.

THE END

Books about William Makepeace Thackeray
Arranged according to their importance
as source material

William Makepeace Thackeray, Lewis Melville. London, J. Lane, 1910.

Thackerayana, Joseph Grego. New York, Scribner's, 1875.

The Letters of William Makepeace Thackeray, (4 vols.), edited with biographical material and notes by Gordon N. Ray. Cambridge, Harvard University Press, 1947.

The Showman of Vanity Fair, Lionel Stevenson. New York, Scribner's, 1947.

Thackeray, Anthony Trollope. New York, Harper's, 1879.

Thackeray as Carthusian, Thomas L. Davies.

Thackeray and His Daughter, Anne Isabella Ritchie. Harper's, New York, 1924.

William Makepeace Thackeray, Charles Whibley. Edinburgh and London, Blackwood, 1903.

The Thackeray Country, Lewis Melville. London, A. & C. Black, 1905.

Thackeray's Haunts and Homes, Eyre Evans Crowe. New York, Scribner's, 1897.

Personal Traits of British Authors, Edward T. Mason. New York, Scribner's, 1885.

Thackeray's London, William H. Rideing. Boston, Cupples, Upham and Co., 1885.

With Thackeray in America, Eyre Evans Crowe. New York, Scribner's, 1893.

Yesterdays with Authors, James T. Fields, Boston, Houghton, 1882.

Playwrights on Playmaking (Thackeray and the Theater), Brander Matthews. New York, Scribner's, 1923.

Eminent English Men and Women in Paris, Roger Boutet de Mouvel. London, D. Nutt, 1912.

Victorian Prose Masters, William Crary Brownell. New York, Scribner's, 1901.

Early Victorian Novelists, Lord David Cecil. Indianapolis, Bobbs-Merrill, 1935.

Essays on Great Writers, Henry Dwight Sedgwick. Boston, Houghton Mifflin, 1903.

The Thackerays in India, Sir William Wilson Hunter. London, H. Frowde, 1897.

Books about Thackeray's Friends and Period

The Life of Edward Fitzgerald, Alfred McKinley Terhune. New Haven, Yale University Press, 1947.

Vauxhall Gardens, James Granville Southworth. Columbia University Press, 1941.

Books by William Makepeace Thackeray

VANITY FAIR	THE VIRGINIANS
YELLOWPLUSH PAPERS	PHILIP
PENDENNIS	DENIS DUVAL
BARRY LYNDON	MISCELLANIES
SKETCH BOOK	A SHABBY GENTEEL STORY
CONTRIBUTIONS TO PUNCH	THE FOUR GEORGES
HENRY ESMOND	ENGLISH HUMORISTS
THE NEWCOMES	MEN'S WIVES
CHRISTMAS BOOKS	

Biographical Edition of Thackeray's Works, edited by Anne Thackeray Ritchie. New York and London, Harper's, 1898.

Thackeray's Complete Works. Boston, Aldine Publishing Co.

The Works of William Makepeace Thackeray. New York, P. F. Collier.